BIOGEOGRAPHY an ecological

and evolutionary approach

BIOGEOGRAPHY an ecological and evolutionary approach

C. BARRY COX PhD DSc
PETER D. MOORE PhD

School of Biological Sciences
King's College, London

THIRD EDITION

BLACKWELL SCIENTIFIC PUBLICATIONS
OXFORD LONDON EDINBURGH MELBOURNE

© 1973, 1976, 1980 by Blackwell
Scientific Publications
Editorial offices:
Osney Mead, Oxford, OX2 OEL
8 John Street, London, WC1N 2ES
9 Forrest Road, Edinburgh, EH1 2QH
214 Berkeley Street, Carlton
   Victoria 3053, Australia

First published 1973
Second edition 1976
Reprinted 1977, 1978
Third edition 1980

British Library
Cataloguing in Publication Data

Cox, Christopher Barry

Biogeography.—3rd ed.
1. Geographical distribution of animals and plants
I. Title II. Moore, Peter Dale
574.9 OH84
ISBN 0-632-00628-5

Distributed in the U.S.A. by
Halsted Press,
a Division of
John Wiley & Sons, Inc.,
New York

Printed in Great Britain by
The Alden Press, Oxford
and bound by
Kemp Hall Bindery
Osney Mead, Oxford

Dedicated to

IAN NEVILL HEALEY
1940–1972

a respected scientist
a stimulating colleague
a valued friend

CONTENTS

PREFACE TO THE FIRST EDITION

Biogeography lies at the meeting-point of several fields of study. To understand why a particular group of organisms is found in a specific area requires knowledge of the organism's ecological relationships—why it is associated with this soil, this temperature range, or this type of woodland. To understand why it is found in particular areas of a continent may require knowledge of the climatic history, which may have led to the isolation of scattered relict communities. Finally, to understand why it is found in some continents and not in others involves knowledge of the evolutionary history of the group itself and of the geological histories of the land-masses, as the processes of continental drift transported them across the globe, splitting them asunder or welding them in new patterns.

As the impact of man upon the Earth's animals and plants increases dramatically, we have become more aware of the need to control the effects of our social and industrial habits. Biogeographers and conservationists therefore now also need to understand how man's present relationship to his environment has come about, and the ways in which he has altered, often radically, the structure of the ecosystems he inhabits or uses.

Despite biogeography's connections with ecology, geography, geology, evolutionary history and economic anthropology, it is usually studied in conjunction with only one or two of these disciplines. Our intention here has been to provide enough of the basic elements of all these approaches, so that a student who specializes in only one of them may nevertheless be able to understand the way in which all of them interact to produce the apparently bewildering array of patterns of distribution of life.

PREFACE TO THE THIRD EDITION

In earlier editions of this book Chapters 1 and 3 were written by Ian Healey, Chapters 4–6 and the pre-Pleistocene part of Chapter 7 by Barry Cox, and the remainder was written by Peter Moore. After Ian Healey's sad, early death, minor revisions were made in the second edition, but this third edition has been extensively rewritten. Peter Moore has incorporated many examples, taken from recent ecological research, into Chapters 1–3; we would like to acknowledge the kind assistance of Dr Stuart McNeill in this. Barry Cox has rewritten much of the chapter on island biogeography, has increased the analysis of animal and, especially, plant historical biogeography, and has extended the integration of these patterns with the processes of continental drift and climatic change. Finally, Peter Moore has widened the treatment of the Ice Ages to embrace the whole world instead of merely northern Europe, and has shown how the mathematical approach to island biogeography can be usefully applied to problems of conservation.

This book attempts to integrate the three main threads of biogeography, which have hitherto remained largely separate. These are ecological biogeography (how organisms live together where they are today), the analytical biogeography of distribution patterns today (where they live, in what diversity, and how they disperse) and historical biogeography (how they came to live where they are today). The last also requires an understanding of modern knowledge of plate tectonics and climatic change. We feel that the proper explanation of the relationship between these topics requires so much space that we cannot deal in greater detail with such topics as mathematical island biogeography. Similarly, to provide more detailed surveys of the patterns of distribution of the families of mammal or flowering plant would add little to the student's understanding of the principles involved, but would merely add to the number of group names, which would either remain poorly comprehended or require lengthy explanations.

C. Barry Cox
Peter D. Moore
October 1979

CHAPTER 1
PATTERNS OF LIFE

Life in all its physical and chemical complexity exists in a multitude of forms, or species. Current estimates show that about 300 000 species of green plants and fungi and about 1 300 000 species of animals have been recognized by biologists. These figures do not include the bacteria and yeasts, of which there are thousands of types, and undoubtedly there are many thousands of species of other groups of organisms remaining to be discovered. None of these forms of life is distributed haphazardly over the surface of the world. Each species occupies only a limited area of part of the world, although the size of the area occupied varies greatly from species to species. There are very rare species that are found in only one or two places, and others that are very common and found almost everywhere. But even the most common species—such as our own *Homo sapiens*—do not live everywhere; very few people live in the polar regions or in desert areas. In fact, unevenness of spatial distribution is as basic a characteristic of living organisms as locomotion or respiration.

Why should this be so? One reason is that, during its history, each species has evolved so that its life processes of physiology, growth and behaviour function efficiently only within a limited range of environmental conditions, and with only certain types of food resources. This is probably a result of the pressures of competition between species for the limited space and food resources available in their environments. Only by ever-increasing specialization in the space it occupies, and the food it uses can a species gain some competitive advantage over others. This process of specialization—adaptation to particular factors or combinations of factors in the environment—is a continuous one, and occurred by the evolutionary process of natural selection, which will be discussed in a later chapter. For the present it can be assumed that because the physical conditions of the organism's environment—temperature, light, wetness or dryness, and so on—and the food resources it contains are far from evenly distributed, the distribution of organisms must also be uneven. Each species therefore has a pattern of distribution related to that of the physical conditions and food resources to which it is adapted.

What is biogeography? The study of the patterns of distribution of organisms in space and time is called *biogeography*. Biologists are nowadays rarely satisfied with the mere description of these patterns, and the biogeographer usually wants to discover which environmental factors are the ones that determine or limit the distribution of the species he studies. To do this he must draw on knowledge from the whole spectrum of the sciences of life and the environment, including geology, geophysics, climatology, palaeontology, plant and animal systematics and taxonomy, evolution, physiology, and ecology. This book is concerned with explaining the distribution of plants and animals, rather than with merely cataloguing them. Its chief aim is to show how the physical environment of a species, its biology, and its evolutionary history interact to bring about its pattern of distribution. But we wish also to show that biogeography is not just an academic science, without relevance to human problems. In the future we shall have to find many new sources of food for our expanding population. Very probably we shall begin to use for food a number of species of animals and plants that we have not previously exploited, or at any rate to change drastically, by selective breeding programmes, the characters and productive capacity of species we already use. (This is already happening extensively with the development of new high-yielding varieties of rice for tropical countries, and of varieties of maize or sweet corn that can grow in cold, wet countries like Britain.) The science of biogeography will often be able to predict whether the species we wish to grow or breed can survive and be productive in environments where they are not normally found, or whether we must develop varieties with new characters such as resistance to drought or cold.

Biogeography is important, too, in fields other than food production. Recently, people have at last begun to realize that the plants and animals that share our environment are not only a resource of economic value, but also a resource of interest and beauty which we have a duty to manage and conserve for future generations just like any other resource, such as food or energy. But the conservation and management of species of animals and plants in natural environments is a complex activity, much more difficult than the management of animals and plants in agriculture. It requires a detailed knowledge of their biology, especially of their geographical distribution, so that we may know in which environments they occur and what conditions they can tolerate. So biogeography is basic to programmes of conservation and management of environments.

As with other aspects of biology, there is no clear point at which biogeography ends and other related sciences, especially ecology, begin. This is because the distribution of a species can be studied on an infinite range of scales from the global to the local. This can be illustrated by reference to a mammal—the European badger (*Meles meles*.)[1] On the global scale, the distribution of the badger covers western and northern Europe as far as the Arctic Circle, Asia Minor, and a zone of central Asia from the Arctic Circle southward to the Himalayas, China, and Japan. Within this huge area of the earth's surface the badger is, of course, very far from evenly distributed. Its patchy distribution is related to a great many factors, but in general the badger is rarest in flat and marshy country and commonest in hilly, wooded areas. In the British Isles, for instance, the badger is most common in southern and western England, and rarest in the east and parts of Ireland and Scotland. Where they occur, badgers most frequently make their burrows or *setts* in woods and copses, especially where these give easy access to the pastureland where badgers often feed, and where the soil is well-drained and suitable for digging. The biologist calls these places where the badger lives its *habitat*. Nearly all animal and plant species seem to have such recognized habitats where they are found more often than in other places.

In the temperate forests of New England, the pin cherry (*Prunus pensylvanicus*) is a frequent species.[2] It is not characteristically found in dense mature forest, but in areas which have been disturbed, either by the death of an old tree or by human activity, where openings in the woodland canopy allow the light to penetrate.

Habitats and microhabitats   For many organisms, especially larger ones, distribution can be conveniently considered in terms of such units of habitat as 'woodland', 'grassland', or 'seashore'. But most species have specific distributions even within such units of the environment as the habitat. The woodland habitat, for instance, consists of a host of smaller *microhabitats*—the humus and leaf-litter layer of the soil, rotting logs, the ground flora zone, the various levels of the tree canopy, tree trunks, and beneath the bark of living trees. Certain characteristic species of animals and plants are found in each of these microhabitats, and so the distribution of these species in woodland coincides more or less closely with that of their microhabitats. Some species are found in more than one of these areas, but generally each species has a particular microhabitat that may be termed its 'headquarters', in which it occurs most frequently and in the highest numbers. Even within habitats that are simpler in structure than woodland—such as grassland—many different microhabitats occur and, as will be explained later, the number of microhabitats present is an important factor determining the number of species that may live in a habitat.

Many quite large and active animals show a tendency to confine themselves to certain parts of a large habitat. The spider monkeys (*Ateles*) of the lowland forests of central and northern South America are active climbers, able to jump long distances, and family groups move about the forest a great deal. If the monkeys are observed over a period of time, however, they can be seen to spend most of their time in the lower parts of the high canopy of the forest, and especially on the smaller peripheral branches of the trees. The reason for this is clear; over 90 per cent of the diet of spider monkeys consists of fruit and nuts, and these food resources will naturally be found most abundantly on the smaller, fast-growing parts of the trees. It is probably best to call areas like these, preferred by a largish, active animal, *minor habitats,* rather than microhabitats, and to keep the latter term for subdivisions with more clearly defined boundaries.

An organism may have two or more contrasting habitats in which it can survive. For example, the sea plantain (*Plantago maritima*), a narrow-leaved European herbaceous plant, is found in salt marshes where it is frequently flooded by sea water, and is also found in mountain habitats where frost constantly disturbs the soils. When faced with the problem of explaining such a strange distribution pattern the biogeographer often has to examine evidence concerning the history of such a species to see what habitats it has occupied in the past. When we do this we find that about 10 000 years ago, at the end of the last Ice Age, the sea plantain was widespread in Europe. With the spread of woodland it was forced into the two dissimilar habitats which it occupies today. What the two habitats have in common is a lack of shading, and it is this which the sea plantain particularly needs from its environment.[3]

Limits of distribution   Whether the areas of a species' distribution are considered on a geographical, habitat, or microhabitat scale, they are surrounded by areas where the species cannot maintain a population because physical conditions or lack of food resources are too different to permit survival. These areas can be viewed as *barriers* that must be crossed by the species if it is to disperse to other favourable, but as yet uncolonized, places—much as the European settlers had to cross ocean barriers to colonize North America or Australia. Any climatic or topographic factor, or combination of factors, may provide a barrier to the distribution of an organism. For example, the problems of locomotion or of obtaining oxygen and food are quite different in water and air. As a result, organisms which are adapted for life on land are unable to cross oceans: their eventual death will be due, in varying proportions, to drowning, to starvation, to exhaustion and to lack of fresh water to drink. Similarly, land is a barrier to organisms that are adapted to life in sea or fresh water, because they require supplies of oxygen dissolved in water rather than as an atmospheric gas, and because they desiccate rapidly in air. Mountain ranges, too, form effective barriers to dispersal because they present extremes of cold too great for many organisms. The amount of rainfall, the rate of evaporation of water from the soil surface, and light intensity are all critical factors limiting the distribution of most green rooted plants. But in all these cases, and in most others, the ultimate barriers are not the hostile factors of the environment but the species' own physiology, which has become adapted to a limited range of environmental conditions. In its distribution a species is therefore the prisoner of its own evolutionary history.

Some plants and animals are confined in their distribution to the areas in which they evolved; these are said to be *endemic* to that region (see p. 19). Their confinement may be due to physical barriers to dispersion, as in the case of many island faunas and floras, or to the fact that they have only recently evolved and have not yet had time to spread from their centres of origin.

At the habitat level, the microhabitats of organisms are surrounded by areas of small-scale variation of physical conditions, or *microclimates*— similar, but on a much smaller scale, to geographical variations in climate —and of food distribution. These form barriers restricting species to their microhabitats. The insects that live in rotting logs, for instance, are adapted by their evolution to a microhabitat with a high water content, and relatively constant temperatures. The logs provide the soft woody materials and micro-organisms they need for food, and also give good protection from predators. Around the logs are areas with fewer, or none, of these desirable qualities and, for many of the animals, attempts to leave their microhabitat would result in death by desiccation, starvation, or predation.

Overcoming the barriers Nevertheless, a few inhabitants of rotting logs do occasionally make the dangerous journey from one log to another, and this shows that few environmental factors are absolute barriers to the dispersal of organisms and that they vary greatly in their effectiveness. Most habitats and microhabitats have only limited resources, and the organisms living in them must have mechanisms enabling them to find new habitats and resources when the old ones become exhausted. These mechanisms often take the form of seeds, resistant stages, or (as in the case of the insects of the rotting-log microhabitat) flying adults with a fairly high resistance to desiccation. There is good evidence that geographical barriers are not completely effective either. When organisms extend their distribution on a geographical scale, it is likely that they are taking advantage of temporary, seasonal, or permanent changes of climate or distribution of habitats that allow them to cross barriers normally closed to them. The British Isles, for instance, lie within the geographical range of about 220 species of birds, but a further 50 or 60 species visit the region as so-called 'accidentals'—these birds do not breed in Britain, but one or two individuals are seen by ornithologists every few years.[4] They come for a variety of reasons: some are blown off-course by winds during migration, others are forced in certain years to leave their normal ranges when numbers are especially high and food is scarce. Many of these accidentals have their true home in North America (such as the pectoral sandpiper (*Calidris melanotos*), a few of which are seen every year) but some come from eastern Asia or even from the Pacific Islands. It is possible, though not very likely, that a few of these chance travellers may in time establish themselves permanently in Europe, as did the collared dove (*Streptopelia decaocto*) which in a few decades has spread from Asia Minor and southern Asia across central Europe and into the British Isles and Scandinavia— perhaps the most dramatic change in distribution known in any verte- brate. This species is often common around the edges of towns and settlements, and seems to depend for food largely on the seeds of weed species common in farms and gardens. Several factors may have interacted to permit this extension of range of the collared dove. Increased human activity during the last century, involving extensive changes in the en- vironment, has produced new habitats and food resources, and it is possible, too, that small changes in climate may have significantly favoured this species. It is, however, considered unlikely that the collared dove would have been able to take advantage of these changes without a change in its own genetic make-up, perhaps a physiological one permitting the species to tolerate a wider range of climatic conditions or to utilize a wider range of food substances.

Improved communications provided by the development of railways in Britain during the 19th century allowed many plant species to spread. Perhaps the best known example is the Oxford ragwort (*Senecio squalidus*) which escaped from the Oxford botanic garden and spread extensively through Britain along the railway routes.[5]

The cases of the collared dove and the Oxford ragwort show how organisms can extend their distribution when new habitats become available. At the present time the human species has such an influence on the ecology of the whole world that new habitats are constantly being created and old ones destroyed. This causes rapid changes in the geographical distribution of many other species. In the past, new habitats became available at a slower rate, through climatic changes, fluctuations in sea-level, glaciation, mountain formation, and erosion, but over long periods of time these slow changes have had a great effect on the distribution of plants and animals.

Biogeographers commonly recognize three different types of pathway by which organisms may spread between one area and another. The first, easiest, pathway is called a *corridor*; such a pathway must include a wide variety of habitats, so that the majority of organisms found at either end of the corridor would find little difficulty in traversing it. The two ends would, therefore, come to be almost identical in their *biota* (i.e. the fauna plus the flora); for example, the great continent of Eurasia that links western Europe to China has acted as a corridor for the dispersal of animals and plants, at least until the recent climatic changes of the Ice Ages. Secondly, the interconnecting region may contain a more limited variety of habitats, so that only those organisms that can exist in these habitats will be able to disperse through it. Such a dispersal route is known as a *filter*; the exclusively tropical lowlands of Central America provide a good example. Finally, some areas are completely surrounded by totally different environments, so that it is extremely difficult for any organism to reach them. The most obvious example is the isolation of islands by wide stretches of sea, but the specially adapted biota of a high mountain peak, of a cave or of a large, deep lake is also extremely isolated from the nearest similar habitat from which colonists might originate. The chances of such a dispersal are therefore extremely low, and largely due to chance combinations of favourable circumstances, such as high winds or floating rafts of vegetation. Such a dispersal route is therefore known as a *sweepstakes route*. It differs from a filter in kind, not merely in degree, for the organisms which traverse a sweepstakes route are not normally able to spend their whole life histories *en route*. Instead, they are alike only in their adaptations to traversing the route, such as those aerial adaptations of spores, light seeds, insects, or birds that enable them to disperse from island to island. Such a biota is therefore not a representative sample of the ecologically integrated, balanced biotas of a normal mainland area, and is said to be *disharmonic*.

A discussion of some patterns of distribution shown by particular species of animals and plants will show how varied and complex these may be, and will help to emphasize the various scales or levels on which such patterns may be considered. In fact, the number of examples that we can choose is quite limited, because the distribution of only a very small number of species has been investigated in detail. Even amongst well-known species, chance finds in unusual places are constantly modifying known distribution patterns and requiring changes in the explanations that biologists give of these patterns.

Some existing patterns are continuous, the area occupied by the group consisting of a single region or of a number of regions which are closely adjacent to one another. These patterns can usually be explained by the distribution of present-day climatic and biological factors; the detailed distributions of several species of dragonfly, and of the plantains, provide good examples (below). Other existing patterns are discontinuous or *disjunct*, the areas occupied being widely separated and scattered over a particular continent, or over the whole world. The organisms which show such a pattern may, like the cycads, be *evolutionary relicts*, the scattered survivors of a once-dominant and widespread group, now unable to compete with newer forms. Others, the *climatic relicts* or *habitat relicts* appear to have been greatly affected by past changes in climate or sea-level. Finally, as will be shown in Chapters 6 and 7, the disjunct patterns of some living groups, and of many extinct groups, have resulted from the physical splitting of a once-continuous area of distribution by the process of continental drift.

The cosmopolitan plantain The broad-leaved plantain, *Plantago major*, has a distribution that could be described as cosmopolitan, because it is found on all the continents except Antarctica[6] (Fig. 1.1). It is typically a species of grassland habitats, and has a rosette of broad leaves pressed close to the soil surface, from which flower-bearing stems rise. Its distribution has not been as thoroughly studied as that of the the dragonflies discussed below, but it appears to be ubiquitous except for the higher

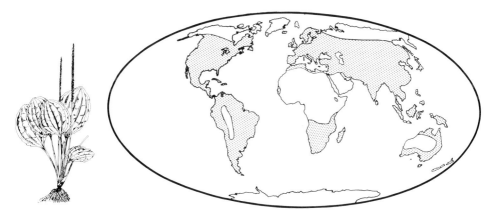

Figure 1.1. The world distribution of a cosmopolitan species, *Plantago major*, the broad-leaved plantain.

northern latitudes and the deserts of North Africa and the Middle East. It has even spread through the East Indies to Australia, New Zealand, and many Pacific islands. On a regional scale the distribution of *P. major* within the British Isles is well known; the species is found almost everywhere and appears to be quite unaffected by variations in climate or in soil conditions—it is found in grassland on both very acid and very alkaline soils. An ecologist would describe this species as an *ecologically tolerant* or *eurytopic* one, because its habitat preferences are so broad. But this alone is not enough to account for its wide distribution; it must have a highly efficient dispersal mechanism. This is provided by its seeds, some of which may be eaten by birds and subsequently dropped in a new habitat. The seeds are resistant to environmental conditions, including those of animals' guts, and at least a proportion of the seeds eaten by animals can germinate after passing through the gut. The seeds also have a coat of mucilage surrounding them, which renders them adhesive. They stick very easily to feathers and fur and may be transported from one place to another in this manner. It is also likely that man has played a part in the dispersal of this plant, because it is quite likely to be mixed with grasses cut for hay and subsequently carried long distances over land or sea. This seems to be its most likely method of transport across the Pacific Ocean to South America. Seeds may also adhere to the tracks and tyres of vehicles and be carried considerable distances overland in this way.

Since *P. major* is not in fact found everywhere, what are the factors limiting its distribution? As with many other organisms, the full answer is not yet known. The plant does not extend far into northern regions, but it is found at quite high altitudes elsewhere, and cold is therefore probably not a limiting factor. It is not found in any really arid areas; its broad leaves offer a large surface for evaporation of water and it may become desiccated in dry climates. Local distribution within its grassland habitat provides some other clues. Figure 1.2 shows the distribution of the areas in which large numbers of plants are found in a meadow; isolated individuals occur elsewhere but cannot be indicated on this scale. In this case the meadow is a hypothetical one, but real examples like it could be found nearly anywhere in Britain. It is obvious that the areas of high abundance are around the gateways and footpaths and in a few other areas where grazing animals might collect. This is because the plantain is most common in places where there is intensive grazing by cattle and trampling by these and other animals, including man. Because of its flattened form it can withstand these pressures better than most grassland plants. *P. major* probably grows best in such places because it needs full sunlight for efficient photosynthesis. In other situations it is usually shaded from sunlight by taller plants and is unable to grow well. The species also tends to be an early colonizer of disturbed, bare soil but is eliminated from such places when other species grow tall. Also its seeds need to be unshaded in order to germinate efficiently. It is this germination and establishment phase which is most sensitive both to climatic stress and to competition. Colonization of the far north by this species is probably prevented by its failure to germinate and establish healthy adult plants in tundra conditions.

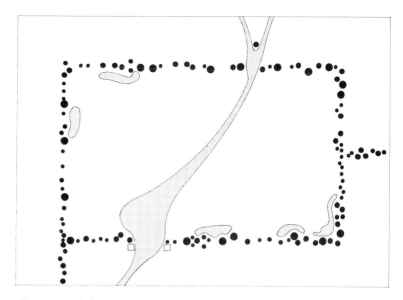

Figure 1.2. A hypothetical example of the distribution of *Plantago major* in a grazed meadow, shown by shaded areas. Isolated individuals of the plant occur elsewhere in the meadow, but large concentrations of the species occur along paths, around gateways, and in other areas that are trampled and disturbed. Black spots represent shrubs and trees.

Patterns of dragonflies   One group of species whose distributions are quite well known, at least in western Europe, are the Odonata, dragonflies and damselflies.[7] The common blue damselfly, *Enallagma cyathigerum,* is possibly one of the most abundant and widely distributed dragonfly species (Fig. 1.3a). In Britain the adults are on the wing in mid-summer, around bodies of fresh water. The female lays eggs in vegetation below the surface of the water and the larvae hatch in a week or two. These live on the bottom of the pond, stream or lake and feed on small crustaceans and insect larvae until they reach a size of 17–18 mm, which may take from two to four years, depending on the quality and quantity of food available. In the May or June after reaching full size, the larvae climb up the stems of *emergent vegetation* (plants rooted in the mud with stem and leaves emerging from the water surface), cast their larval skins, and emerge as winged adults. *E. cyathigerum* is found in a wide range of freshwater habitats, including both still and moving water, though it is perhaps least common in fast-moving water, or in places where silt is being deposited. Probably the ideal habitat for this species is a fairly large body of still water with plenty of floating vegetation, such as pondweed (*Potamogeton*), and with a good growth of shore-weed (*Littorella uniflora*) or water milfoil (*Myriophyllum alterniflorum*) rooted around the edges and on the bottom. None of these requirements is at all rigid, however, and big populations often occur elsewhere. *Enallagma cyathigerum* is found in both acid and alkaline waters, and often occurs in brackish pools on salt marshes. As a

Figure 1.3. The distribution on a world scale and within the British Isles of three species of dragonfly. (a) *Enallagma cyathigerum*, (b) *Sympetrum sanguineum*, and (c) *Anax imperator*.

result, clearly, this species is eurytopic, like *Plantago*. It is found almost everywhere in the British Isles, being absent only from Snowdonia, parts of the Pennines, and lowland and north-east Scotland.

The geographical distribution of this damselfly is also very wide. In Europe the distribution lies mostly between 45°N and the Arctic Circle, although it includes some of the wetter parts of Spain, and is rather scattered in northern Scandinavia; it is not found in Greenland or Iceland. The species is found in a few places in North Africa, in Asia Minor, and around the Caspian Sea. Large areas of Asia south of the Arctic Circle also fall within its range. In North America it is found everywhere north of about 35–40°N to the Arctic Circle, except Labrador and Baffin Island. Populations also occur in the ideal habitats provided by the Everglades of Florida, which mark the species' furthest southward expansion. The broad geographical distribution of this species is almost certainly due to its ecological tolerance and ability to make use of a wide range of habitats in very different climates. This type of distribution pattern, a belt around the

Patterns of Life

Northern Hemisphere, is shown by many species of animals and plants, and is termed *circumboreal*—'around the northern regions'. The frequency of this pattern in very different organisms suggests that the two northern land-masses may once have been joined, enabling certain species to spread right around the hemisphere.

As *E. cyathigerum* is so successful, one might ask why it has not spread further southward. One reason may be the relative scarcity of watery habitats in the subtropical regions immediately to the south of its present range— the arid areas of Central America, North Africa, and central Asia. The species is perhaps not robust enough for the long migrations that would be needed to reach suitable habitats in the Southern Hemisphere (there are very few wind belts that might assist such a migration). Another possibility is that there are other species already occupying all the habitats that *E. cyathigerum* could colonize further south. These species may be better adapted to the physical conditions of their habitats than *E. cyathigerum* and could therefore compete successfully with it for the available food resources; this might exclude the species from these areas. In fact in the Southern Hemisphere there are many species of the genus *Enallagma* and the closely related genus *Ischnura* that might be expected to have similar habitat and food requirements to *E. cyathigerum*; there are at least eight species of *Enallagma* in South Africa alone. Any of these explanations, or a combination of them, would explain why the common blue damselfly is confined to the high latitudes of the Northern Hemisphere.

The distribution of *E. cyathigerum* may be contrasted with that of the beautiful dragonfly *Sympetrum sanguineum,* sometimes called the ruddy sympetrum (Fig. 1.3b). This species has a limited distribution in western Europe, parts of Spain, a few places in Asia Minor and North Africa, and around the Caspian Sea; it is not found in eastern Asia or North America. In Britain the species is found in only the southern and eastern parts of England, a few places in Wales, and parts of south-eastern Ireland. These areas lie on the northern edge of its distribution, and even here numbers are supplemented by regular immigration of adults from Europe, for the species can fly strongly. The reason for the limited distribution of this dragonfly is almost certainly that the larva has very precise habitat requirements. The larva is found in ditches and ponds with still waters, but only where certain emergent plants—the great reedmace (*Typha latfolia*) and horsetails (*Equisetum*)—are growing. Why the larva should have these precise requirements is not clear, because it is certainly not a herbivore, and feeds on insect larvae and crustaceans, but so far the larvae have never been found away from the roots of these plants. *Sympetrum sanguinum* could therefore be described as a *stenotopic* species—one with very limited ecological tolerance. The fact that it can colonize only a very few habitats must certainly have limited its distribution, but other, unknown, factors are also at work, for the species is often absent from waters in which reedmace or horsetails are present.

The northern distribution of these two species may be contrasted with that of the emperor dragonfly, *Anax imperator*[8] (Fig. 1.3c). The adults of this species are 8–10 cm long, and the larva is found typically in large ponds and lakes and in slow-moving canals and streams; it is a voracious predator and can eat animals as big as fish larvae. Britain lies on the northern edge of the geographical range of this species, where it is found only in the south and east, especially where there are many reservoirs and artificial ponds. The distribution covers a band of Europe between about 55°N and 40°N but, unlike the other two species, it is well-distributed on the North African coast and the Nile Valley and stretches across Asia Minor to north-west India. It even spreads across the Sahara Desert down into Central Africa, where there are suitable habitats such as Lake Chad and the lakes of East Africa, and it is found in most parts of South Africa except the Kalahari Desert. (It is possible that the South African populations may belong to a separate subspecies from the European forms.)

So the distribution of *A. imperator* is confined to the Old World and does not extend far into Asia. It appears to be basically a Mediterranean and subtropical species whose good powers of flight and fairly broad ecological tolerance have enabled it to cross the unfavourable areas of North Africa to new habitats in southern Africa. No doubt favourable habitats for *A. imperator* do occur in the other land masses (although there may be potential competitors there, of course), but the dragonfly cannot now reach them because the land connections lie to the north, where its distribution seems limited.

In most tropical dragonfly species the larvae emerge from the water and metamorphose to the adult at night; they are very vulnerable to predators at the time of emergence, and darkness probably affords some protection from birds. But the process of metamorphosis in inhibited by cold temperatures, and in northern Europe many species are compelled by low night temperatures to undergo at least part of their emergence in daylight, when birds eat large numbers of them. This probably puts a northern limit ot the distribution of many species of dragonfly, including *A. imperator*, which would explain why this species has not been able to invade the Americas or eastern Asia.

The maps in Figure 1.3 illustrate the contrast in the distribution of these three species of dragonfly. Even within the British Isles they show very different distributions. This is because all three exhibit, to varying degrees and for a number of different reasons, contrasting preferences for particular habitats. As a result of their geographical position on the north-west corner of a great land mass, the British Isles have a complex and variable pattern of climate which interacts with a varied geology to produce a range of types of habitat surprisingly wide for so small an area of the world. Species like these dragonflies reflect this complexity in their own patterns of distribution in Britain.

Cycads—evolutionary relics   The cycads (family Cycadaceae) are a group of very curious plants; there are nine genera and about 100 species, all of which are very rare and have a very limited and restricted distribution.[9] Most cycads are trees with a single, short, unbranched stem or trunk crowned with a fringe of fern-like leaves, and in general appearance they are not unlike palm trees (Fig. 1.4). A few rather unusual species have the stem buried in the soil with only the top 4 cm and the leaves showing at the surface. There are no flowers, and the seeds are carried on structures similar to pine cones; these do not attract insects, and cycads depend on wind for pollination. The entire group is confined to tropical and subtropical regions[10] and, even where they are found, the species are never very common. Cycads are thought to grow very slowly and many plants may be more than 1000 years old. The distributions of individual species are too limited to show on a world map, but Figure 1.5 shows the composite distribution of all the species. Four genera are found in North, South and Central America, with two of them confined to Mexico, one species to a small area of western Cuba and another to southern Florida. The largest genus, *Cycas*, has a number of rare species in Australia, India, China, southern Japan, various Pacific islands and Madagascar. Because of their curiosity value, cycads are often grown in ornamental gardens in warm parts of the world, but these planted trees do not, of course, form part of the natural geographical distribution.

How can the rarity and patchy distribution of the cycads be explained?

Figure 1.4. A cycad, *Cycas circinalis,* from south-east Asia. (Photograph by Heather Angel.)

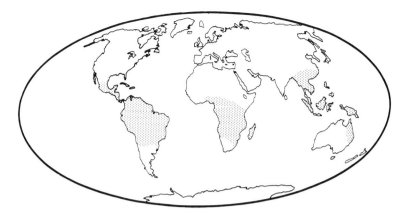

Figure 1.5. The world distribution of living species of cycads. The cycads as a whole show a scattered distribution, mainly in tropical regions, and are the remnants of a group that was much more widely distributed in the Mesozoic. Even within the range shown most cycads are rather rare.

Biogeographers must draw on knowledge from other fields—in this case from palaeobotany, the study of fossil plants—to understand the distribution of an organism. Palaeobotanists have found many plant fossils similar to the living cycads in rocks that were deposited during the Mesozoic Era, between about 225 million and 65 million years ago. These fossils suggest that the ancestors of modern cycads were not only much more common than their descendants but also much more widely distributed. Fossils of whole groups of cycad species that probably grew together as plant communities—'fossil floras'—have been found in such widely separated places as Oregon, Siberia, Greenland, Sweden, central Europe, Italy, and Australia, and it is likely that their range was even wider than this list suggests. No such communities of cycad species are found anywhere today; isolated groups of single species are found here and there. Of the places mentioned above where fossil cycads have been found, only Australia now has living representatives.

It seems that cycads were amongst the most important elements of the vegetation in Mesozoic times—the age of the dinosaurs—and it has been suggested that some of the herbivorous dinosaurs browsed extensively on cycads, much as herbivorous mammals feed on flowering plants and trees today. Since the end of the Mesozoic Period, the cycads have been reduced to a remnant of their former number of species and extent of distribution. They have been replaced largely by flowering plants (angiosperms) that probably evolved from fern-like ancestors toward the end of the Palaeozoic Era, but became common only in the late Mesozoic. The cycads had less efficient reproduction, and possibly much slower growth, than these newer forms and were unable to compete with the flowering plants for space and light. In recent times efforts have been made to eradicate cycads from some grazing lands because of their toxicity to animals.[10]

Since the Mesozoic, tropical climates have been restricted to the equatorial regions and, because the cycads were probably always species of warm environments, this contraction of their habitat must also have been disadvantageous to them. With low rates of reproduction and slow growth, cycads were probably unable to adapt to new conditions fast enough to keep up with climatic changes. The modern species are evolutionary relicts whose distribution is limited to parts of the world where conditions are most suitable for them—they can then compete fairly successfully with flowering plants. Many of the areas where cycads survive are isolated geographically, and this may have protected them to some extent against competition from some of the most recently evolved and vigorous groups of flowering plants that have not yet been able to exploit these isolated regions fully. The ability of the floating seeds of *Cycas* to survive even a prolonged stay in sea water has also made it possible for that genus to disperse to many Pacific islands.

Climatic relicts   Many other species, which in the past were widely distributed, were affected by climatic changes and survive now only in a few 'islands' of favourable climate. Such species are called *climatic relicts*—they are not necessarily species with long evolutionary histories, since many major climatic changes have occurred quite recently. The Northern Hemisphere has an interesting group of *glacial relict* species whose distributions have been modified by the northward retreat of the great ice sheets that extended as far south as the Great Lakes in North America, and to Germany in Europe, during the Pleistocene Ice Ages (the last glaciers retreated from Britain about 10 000 years ago). Many species that were adapted to cold conditions at that time had distributions to the south of the ice sheets almost as far as the Mediterranean. Now that these areas are much warmer, these species survive there only in the coldest places, usually at high altitudes in mountain ranges, and the greater part of their distribution lies far to the north in Scandinavia, Scotland, or Iceland. In some cases, species even appear to have become extinct in northern regions and are represented now only by glacial relict populations in the south.

An interesting glacial relict is the springtail, *Tetracanthella arctica* (Insecta, Collembola).[11] This dark blue insect, only about 1·5 mm long, lives in the surface layers of the soil and in clumps of moss and lichens, where it feeds on dead plant tissues and fungi. It is quite common in the soils of Iceland and Spitzbergen, and has also been found further west in Greenland and in a few places in Arctic Canada. Outside these truly Arctic regions, it is known to occur in only two regions; in the Pyrenean Mountains between France and Spain, and in the Tatra Mountains on the borders of Poland and Czechoslovakia (with isolated finds in the nearby Carpathian Mountains) (Fig. 1.6). In these mountain ranges the species is found at altitudes of around 2000 m in Arctic and sub-Arctic conditions. It is hard to imagine that the species can have colonized these two areas from its main centre further north, because it has very poor powers of distribution (it is quickly killed by low humidity or high temperatures) and is not

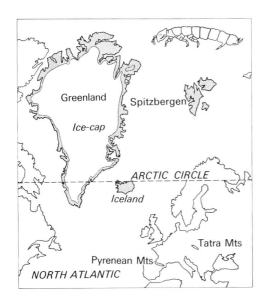

Figure 1.6. The springtail *Tetracanthella arctica*, and a map of its distribution. It is found mostly in northern regions, but populations exist in the Pyrenees and in mountains in central Europe. These populations were isolated at these cold, high altitudes when the ice sheet retreated northwards at the end of the Ice Ages.

likely to have been transported there accidentally by man. The likely explanation of the two southern populations is that they are remnants of a much wider distribution in Europe in the Ice Ages. But it is surprising that *T. arctica* has not been found at high altitudes in the Alps, despite careful searching by entomologists. Perhaps it has simply not yet been noticed, or perhaps it used to occur there but has since died out. One interesting feature of this species is that, whereas animals from the Arctic and the Tatras have eight small eyelets (*ocelli*) on either side of the head, specimens from the Pyrenees have only six. This suggests that the Pyrenean forms have undergone some evolutionary changes since the end of the Ice Ages while they have been isolated from the rest of the species, and perhaps they should be classified as a separate subspecies.

A plant example of a glacial relict (see Fig. 1.7) is the Norwegian mugwort (*Artemisia norvegica*), a small alpine plant now restricted to Norway, the Ural Mountains and two isolated localities in Scotland. During the last glaciation and immediately following it, the plant was widespread, but it became restricted in distribution as forest spread.

There are probably several hundred species of both animals and plants in Eurasia that are glacial relicts of this sort, and they include many species that, in contrast to the springtail, have quite good powers of distribution. One such species is the mountain or varying hare, *Lepus timidus*, a seasonally variable species (its fur is white in the winter and bluish for the rest of the year), which is closely related to the more common brown hare, *L. europaeus*. The varying hare has a circumboreal distribution around the

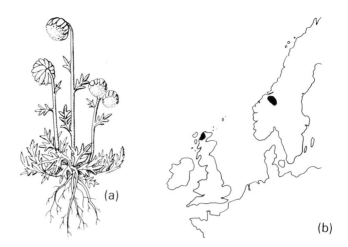

Figure 1.7. The Norwegian mugwort, *Artemisia norvegica*: (a) the plant, (b) distribution map showing its restricted range in only two mountainous areas of Europe.

northern parts of the world, including Scandinavia, Siberia, northern Japan and northern Canada (although the North American forms are thought by some zoologists to form a separate species, *L. americanus*). The southernmost part of the main distribution is in Ireland and the southern Pennines of England, but there is a glacial relict population living in the Alps that differs in no important features from those in the more northerly regions. There is however, an interesting complication—*L. timidus* is found all over Ireland, thriving in a climate that is no colder than that of many parts of continental western Europe. There seems to be no climatic reason why this hare should not have a wider distribution, but it is probably excluded from many areas by its inability to compete with its close relative, the brown hare, for food resources and breeding sites. Relict populations of the varying hare survive in the Alps because, of the two species, it is the better adapted to cold conditions.[12]

One very remarkable example of a glacial relict is the dung beetle species *Aphodius holdereri* (Fig. 1.8). This beetle is now restricted to the

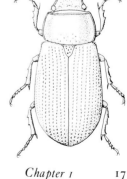

Figure 1.8. *Aphodius holdereri*, a dung beetle now found in the high plateau of Tibet.

high Tibetan plateau (3000–5000 m), having its southern limit at the northern slopes of the Himalayas. In 1973, G. R. Coope of Birmingham University in England found the remains of at least 150 individuals of this species in a peaty deposit from a gravel pit at Dorchester-on-Thames in southern England.[13] The deposit dated from the middle of the last glaciation, and subsequently 14 sites have yielded remains of this species in Britain, all dating between 25 000 and 40 000 years ago. Evidently *A. holdereri* was then a widespread species, but climatic changes have severely restricted the availability of suitable habitats for its survival. Only the remote Tibetan mountains now provide *Aphodius* with the extreme climatic conditions necessary for its survival.

The Ice Age closed with a sudden warming of the climate, and the glaciers retreated northwards; behind them came the plant and animal species that had been driven south during glacial times. Warmth-loving animals, particularly insects, were able to move northward rapidly. Plants were slower in their response, because their rate of spread is slower. Seeds were carried northward, germinated, grew, and finally flowered and sent out more seeds to populate the bare northlands. As this migration continued, melting glaciers produced vast quantities of water that poured into the seas, and the ocean-levels rose. Some of the early colonizers reached areas by land connections that were later severed by rising sea-levels.

The maritime fringe of western Europe must have provided a particularly favourable migration route for southern species during the period following the retreat of the glaciers. Many warmth-loving plants and animals from the Mediterranean region moved northward along this coast and penetrated at least as far as the south-west of Ireland, before the English Channel and the Irish Sea had risen to form physical barriers to such movement. The nearness of the sea, together with the influence of the warm Gulf Stream, gives western Ireland a climate that is wet, mild, and frost-free, and this has allowed the survival of certain Mediterranean plants that are scarce or absent in the rest of the British Isles. For example, *Arbutus unedo* (the strawberry tree) is found growing wild nowhere else in Britain, yet it is quite common in western Ireland, especially in County Kerry and County Cork. It also occurs in western Brittany, but its real stronghold is the Mediterranean region, especially Spain and Portugal. Like many Mediterranean trees and shrubs, the strawberry tree is *sclerophyllous*, which means it has hard, leathery leaves (see Fig. 1.9). This is a plant adaptation often associated with arid climates. Flowering in many plant species is triggered by a response to a particular daylength—this is called *phtotoperiodism*. *Arbutus* flowers in autumn, as the length of night is increasing, and this is an adaptation which is again associated with Mediterranean conditions, since at this season the summer drought gives way to a warm, damp period. The flowers, which are cream-coloured, conspicuous, and bell-shaped, have nectaries that attract insects, and in Mediterranean areas they are pollinated by long-tongued insects such as bees, which are plentiful in late autumn. In Ireland, however, insects are scarce in the autumn and pollination is therefore much less certain. Thus the strawberry tree reached Ireland soon after the retreat of the

Patterns of Life

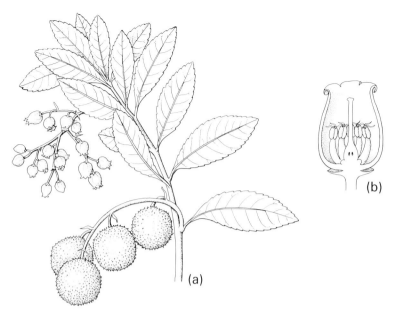

(b)

(a)

Figure 1.9. The strawberry tree, *Arbutus unedo*: (a) plant showing leathery leaves, and swollen fruits which are red in colour; (b) cross-section of a flower.

glaciers and has since been isolated there as a result of rising oceans. Although the climate has steadily grown colder since its first colonization, *Arbutus* has so far managed to hold its own and survive in this outpost of its range.

Endemic organisms   Because each new species of organism evolves in one particular, restricted area, its distribution will be limited by the barriers that surround its area of origin. Each such area will, therefore, contain organisms that are found there and nowhere else; these organisms are said to be *endemic* to that area. As time goes by more and more organisms will evolve within the area, and the percentage of its biota that is endemic is therefore a good guide to the length of time for which an area has been isolated (see also pp. 136 and 171).

As these organisms continue to evolve they will also become progressively more and more different from their relatives in other areas. Taxonomists are likely to recognize this by raising the taxonomic rank of the organisms concerned. So, for example, after 2 million years the biota of an isolated area might contain only a few endemic species. After 10 million years the descendants of these species might be so unlike their nearest relatives in other areas that they might be placed in one or more endemic genera. After 35 million years these genera might appear to be so different from their nearest relatives as to be placed in a different family, and so on. (The absolute times that would be involved would, of course, vary and depend upon the rate of evolution of the group in question.) So, the longer an area has been isolated, the higher the taxonomic rank of its endemic organisms is likely to be, and vice versa.

Figure 1.10 shows the proportion of the montane flora in various European mountain ranges that are endemic to their particular area. It is evident that the more northerly of the mountain ranges shown have a lower proportion of their flora which is endemic whereas the southern, Mediterranean mountains, have higher proportions.[14]

The montane plants, like the glacial relicts described above, are now limited in range because of the increasing warmth of the last 10 000 years. The northern mountains may be poorer in endemics simply because local glaciation there was more severe and some of the species surviving further south became extinct. On the other hand, the richness of the southern mountains could be explained by the fact that the geographical barriers

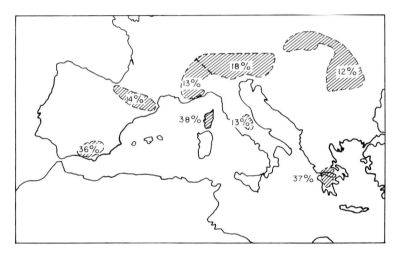

Figure 1.10. The percentage of endemic plants in the floras of the mountain ranges of southern Europe. (From Favarger, 1972.[14])

between the northern montane blocks are less severe (less distance, no sea barriers) and hence migration and sharing of mountain floras is more likely than in the south, where barriers are considerable.

In general, there are two major factors influencing the degree of endemism in an area; these are isolation and stability. Thus, isolated islands and mountains are often rich in endemics. Long-term climatic stability is rather rare, but there is evidence that some parts of the earth have been more stable than others. For example, the Cuatro Ciénegas basin in Mexico appears to have retained a very stable vegetation over the last 40 000 years, judging from the evidence of pollen from lake cores collected in the area (see Chapter 8). This basin is also rich in endemic organisms.[15]

California is another region which is very rich in endemics, and this is again a somewhat isolated area, with high mountains and deserts separating it from most of the rest of America. Once more it is possible to relate some of the endemics to long survival in isolated areas. On the other hand, many plant species in California are undergoing rapid evolution, and new types are arising in such plant genera as *Aquilegia* and *Clarkia*. These so-called '*neoendemics*' (as opposed to the ancient '*palaeoendemics*') may be restricted simply because they have not had time to expand their ranges into other areas. G. L. Stebbins and J. Major proposed that the Californian palaeoendemics were restricted mainly to either wet or arid areas, whereas the neoendemics were found mainly in less predictable habitats, and more recent work has supported this idea.[16]

Microhabitat   Having discussed the reasons underlying the distribution patterns on a world scale and on a country-wide scale, one can finally turn to examine the small-scale pattern of distribution, within a single habitat. It is common to find, living together within a habitat, several quite closely related species with similar requirements for food and space. If their distribution is examined in detail, it is almost always found that each species is living in a distinct microhabitat within the habitat as a whole. As will be seen in Chapter 3, it is probable that this situation has evolved so that the food resources and living space of the habitat can be shared out among its habitats without severe competition.

In an area of deciduous woodland in Britain, it is possible, especially in the south, to find as many as 12 or 13 species of harvest spider (Order Opiliones). These are similar in general appearance to true spiders (Order Araneae), with eight long, jointed legs, but the body is a single mass, rather than divided in two by a thin waist as in true spiders. Harvest spiders are 1 cm or less in length, and are voracious predators of any arthropods smaller than themselves, especially fly larvae, springtails and aphids, and also often eat other species of spider and their own young. The distribution of 11 species is shown in Figure 1.11.

With the exception of *Megabunus diadema*, which is scarce in some places, all these species are quite common in Britain and most have a wide distribution in Europe. Temperate, deciduous woodland has a distinctly stratified structure; it can be divided into four distinct divisions—the tree canopy and branches; the shrub layer of small trees up to 3 m high (which includes the trunks of taller trees); the herb layer, with plants such as dog's mercury (*Mercurialis perennis*) or bluebells (*Endymion non-scriptus*); and the ground layer, containing leaf litter, mosses, stones, dead wood and so on. Each of these divisions or horizontal layers in fact contains many microhabitats, but harvest spiders are quite large and active animals and their distribution cannot be considered on a small scale. Each species has one or two levels at which it is found much more frequently than elsewhere, as shown in Figure 1.11.

The herb layer contains many more species than the other layers, probably because it is more varied in structure than the others and contains more small-scale microhabitats. Three of these species are rather different from the others in their behaviour. The immature individuals of

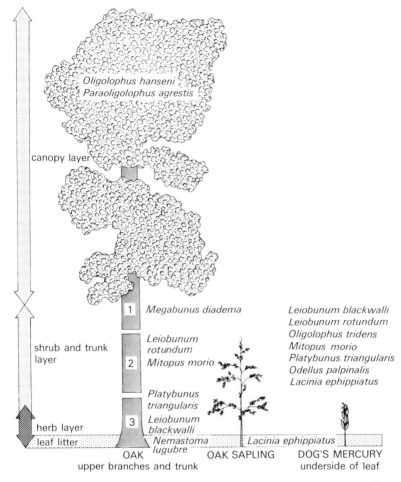

Figure 1.11. A model of the distribution of 11 species of harvest spider (order Opiliones) in woodland in southern England. Each species is most common in one or more microhabitats within the habitat, but is sometimes to be found elsewhere.

Leiobunum rotundum spend the spring in the herb layer, but at about the end of June they move to tree trunks, where they spend the day about 10 m above ground level. At night, however, they leave the tree trunks and return to the herb layer to hunt, so the species has separate microhabitats for nesting and for feeding. *L. blackwalli* also is found on tree trunks as well as in the herb layer, but is not known to migrate like *L. rotundum*, and tends to occur rather lower on the trunks. A third species, *Mitopus morio*, is found in all microhabitats except the soil and the higher parts of the canopy, and this wide distribution is probably related to the fact that it is largely a predator of other harvest spiders. Not all seven species are likely to be present and competing for resources at the same time—their periods of activity are rather spread out through the year. The species showing perhaps the strongest habitat preference is *Nemastoma lugubre*, which is

Patterns of Life

found only in leaf litter and humus. The English ecologist, Dr Valerie Todd, made an interesting study of the ecology of harvest spiders and, in particular, of their reactions to the relative humidity (water content) of the air in their habitats. In a careful experimental study, Dr Todd offered the various species a choice of environments with different atmospheric humidities.[17] She found that those species which live in very humid microhabitats, such as *N. lugubre* which lives in the litter layer, or *Oligolophus tridens,* which lives in the ground vegetation, tended to select the most humid environments. Species like *Leiobunum rotundum* and *L. blackwalli,* which live mostly in less humid places above the ground vegetation, selected drier environments. The species normally found in drier places, up on the branches of trees, such as *Oligolophus hanseni* and *Paraoligolophus agrestis,* selected the most dry environments. These experiments suggest that the harvest spiders are adapted to the atmosphere of the microhabitats where they are most common, and that they suffer physiological stress elsewhere, by dehydration in drier places and by wetting in moister places. They are therefore limited to their microhabitats by their own physiology; this problem will be considered in more detail in Chapter 2.

One finds a similar pattern exhibited by the plants which inhabit oak forests, especially those which live *epiphytically* upon the oak trees. This group, which use the trees as a support on which to grow yet do not act as parasites, includes various mosses, lichens and algae.[18] The chief microhabitats in which some of these epiphytic plants live are shown in Figure 1.12. Some lichen species occupy coarse bark and therefore do not grow and compete well on fine twigs; others form bushy growths from strong attachment organs and consequently are able to maintain growth even on the more supple twigs. Most mosses (and some ferns) are restricted to the thicker branches or main trunk and they usually dominate the base of the tree.

Since plants do not select their microhabitat by movement in the way that most animals do, but rather by failing to survive when it is unsuitable, one cannot conduct the kind of preference experiment which was possible with the harvest spiders. One can, however, grow the plants under various conditions in an experimental situation. When this is done, we find that some require more moisture for active growth than others. Many cannot maintain photosynthesis adequately at relative humidities of less than 90 per cent. Such plants are usually restricted to the sheltered regions near the ground.

The body of a tree thus creates a whole range of microhabitats by its own spatial complexity. It does this by modifying the local climates experienced beneath its canopy and within its branches. Figure 1.12 shows the way in which wind speeds can be altered by the presence of a tree; this in turn would affect temperature and humidity, as also would the diminishing light intensity as one passes down through the canopy.[19] Local distribution patterns of plants and animals are often strongly influenced by the effects of *microclimate.* Even within the much less complex canopy of a grassland habitat there may be a considerable degree

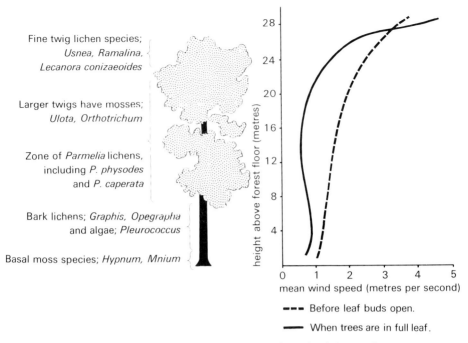

Figure 1.12. On the right, the graphs of wind speed at different levels in an oak forest show that the wind is more able to penetrate into lower levels of the forest before the leaves open. (After Geiger, 1955.[19]) Patterns of lichen distribution on a tree are indicated on the left.

of microclimatic variation with distance above the ground surface, as can be seen in Figure 1.13.

The distribution of harvest spiders, with each species having one or more microhabitats as a 'headquarters', but sometimes occurring elsewhere in the habitat, is probably typical of most groups of animals in most habitats. The same is probably true for plant species, such as *Plantago major*, already discussed, which grows best and is most common on open, trampled areas of a meadow although isolated individuals may occur in other places. Moist habitats contain plant species, such as mosses, which are adapted to live in their wetter or more shaded parts. However, the degree to which a species is adapted and restricted to a particular habitat or microhabitat varies greatly amongst both plant and animal species. A few general tendencies can be recognized. For instance, plant species such as trees, that are big and slow-growing and which themselves exert a great influence on the form and structure of the habitat, tend to show less strict habitat or microhabitat preferences than small and delicate species such as herbs and mosses.

Amongst animals, there are broad differences between predators and herbivores. Predatory animals are usually active, relatively large species and are often not very specific in their food requirements, so they often tend to have rather broad microhabitat preferences. Herbivores, on the

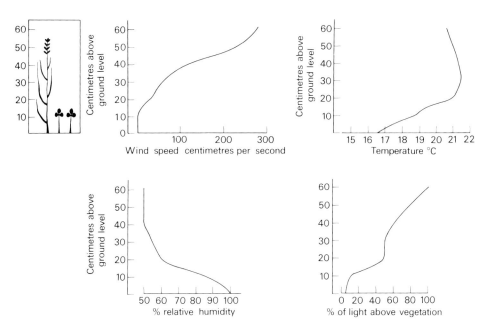

Figure 1.13. Diagram showing the structure of grassland vegetation and the effect which this has upon the microclimate of the habitat.

other hand, are less mobile and often more specific in their food requirements and, of the species in a habitat, these are usually the ones with the most precise microhabitat preferences.

Distribution and food   The distribution of an animal may be very closely related to that of the food it eats. A particularly interesting example is that of the Chalkhill blue butterfly, *Lysandra coridon,* which is on the wing in July, August, and September.[20] In Britain it is found only in relatively few areas in southern England, although it is widespread in mainland Europe. When the distribution is analysed, it is found to coincide closely with areas of countryside underlain with chalk in central southern England (Fig. 1.14). Why should the range of *L. coridon* be related to the geology of the land in this way? The most significant factor in determining this pattern is that the caterpillar larva of this butterfly usually feeds on only one plant, *Hippocrepis comosa,* the horseshoe vetch, which is itself rather uncommon. This plant is one of a group called *calcicoles,* which are able to grow well only on chalky or limestone-rich soils. The vetch is a perennial plant that develops a mat of foliage up to 1 m or so across and 30 cm high. The caterpillars of the Chalkhill blue feed most actively on the leaves of the plant during May and June. When fully developed they drop to the soil, crawl into cracks, and metamorphose into pupae. After one or two weeks the adults emerge from the pupae, crawl up the vegetation and, after drying their wings, take flight. The females lay

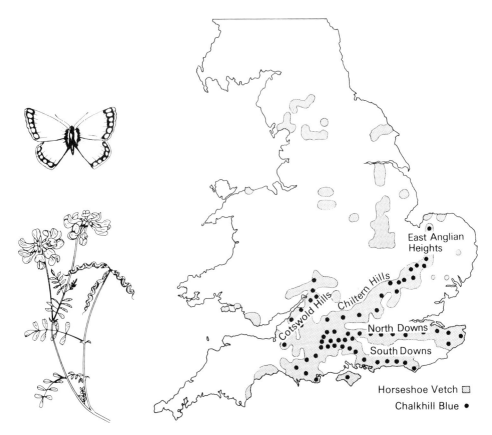

Figure 1.14. The distribution in the British Isles of the Chalkhill blue butterfly, *Lysandra coridon* (each dot representing an area where the species is known to breed), and of its foodplant, the horseshoe vetch, *Hippocrepis comosa.*

eggs on the leaves of the vetch, which hatch into caterpillars in the following April, and these live on the plant throughout the summer, growing rapidly; thus the life cycle repeats itself.

The reason why calcicoles such as the horseshoe vetch will grow only on chalk and limestone soils has been the subject for a considerable amount of ecological research. These soils are rich in calcium carbonate, which produces a very alkaline environment for the plant roots. Under these conditions, only the calcicole plants appear to be able to absorb all of the mineral ions necessary for active growth, such as phosphorus, potassium, iron, etc. The precise adaptations involved are probably associated with the structure and chemistry of their cell membranes through which the ions pass.[21] Plants possessing such adaptations have a considerable competitive advantage over those which do not, and exclude them from these extreme habitats. The horseshoe vetch is one of these especially adapted plants—experiments show that its roots grow much faster in chalky soils than in others. This would explain the limited distribution of the vetch and hence of its dependent herbivore, the butterfly. But other problems remain, because the distribution of the butterfly is not as wide as that of its food plant. Not only is the Chalkhill blue absent from many places in the south where the vetch occurs, but it is not present (except very occasionally) in any of its food plant's more northern habitats on limestone. In the south the butterfly appears to be more common on south-facing slopes of the Downs, and it may be that it can live only in these warmer habitats that get plenty of sun. Since the Chalkhill blue is more common in Europe, it is probably a Mediterranean species that, in the southern parts of the British Isles, is at the northern limit of its distribution. The Chalkhill blue also has a curious relationship with some species of ant, especially the yellow meadow ant, *Lasius flavus*. These ants drink a sugary fluid produced by glands on the bodies of the caterpillars, and in return they protect them from insect predators and spiders, and sometimes even carry them to more favourable locations of their food plants. This ant is known to be able to build its nest only in certain situations and on certain soils. Thus it may be that, because of their peculiar relationship, the distribution of the Chalkhill blue is limited by that of the ant, as well as by the distribution of the vetch.

There remains the problem of why the butterfly should be limited to a single food plant. One might expect this to be a disadvantage because, as in this case, the distributions of many plant species are limited by geology and soil, and by climatic factors. Ecologists think that, in most cases, animals feeding on a single food plant are not limited to it by special nutritional requirements that it alone provides. More probably, such animals gain a competitive advantage over others by being especially adapted to exploit a single food source with maximum efficiency, despite the fact that this has disadvantages if the distribution of the plant is limited. The host plant may provide favourable physical conditions, and many insects have also developed special camouflages, effective only against the background provided by one food plant. Also, herbivores probably 'recognize' their food plants by the presence of particular chemical compounds, usually not themselves of nutritional importance. These 'token stimuli' are especially important to species limited to a single food plant, but what these factors are in the case of the Chalkhill blue is not known.

Soils and plants Unlike animals, green plants do not depend upon other organisms as a source of food. They obtain energy direct from sunlight and their requirements for inorganic materials are supplied by the atmosphere (in the case of carbon dioxide) and the soil. Light intensity is therefore an important habitat factor for plants (as in the case of *Plantago major*) and so are the soil conditions. We have seen that the horseshoe vetch will occur only on alkaline soils, because only under these conditions is it able to compete adequately for inorganic nutrients, and many other plants have similarly precise requirements.

Soils differ in the abundance of different nutrients they contain (usually the products of parent rock weathering), in the size of particles of which they are composed (which influences such characteristics as drainage properties and nutrient retention) and the form of the organic matter (either well mixed, or stratified on the surface). From the plant's point of view, survival means the ability to grow and compete successfully under the prevailing conditions of climate and soil. Soil conditions are thus of considerable importance in determining a plant's potential distribution.

As a good example of a plant which has rather specific soil requirements we can take the stinging nettle, *Urtica dioica*. This is a common plant of all the temperate regions of the world and, like the broad-leaved plantain, it is often associated with habitats where man's influence is strong. For example, it is often associated with rubbish dumps, manure heaps, and areas where domestic animals rest or shelter. There are some habitats which are not strongly influenced by man and yet in which it grows successfully, such as damp woodlands and riversides. Evidently, the stinging nettle is tolerant of a wide range of soil wetness, occurring in both swamp situations and in dry grasslands. What other factors are likely to be affecting its distribution?

C. D. Pigott and K. Taylor[22] investigated this problem in a limestone area of the English midlands, where the stinging nettle appeared to be most frequent on the lower slopes of the valley sides, as shown in Figure 1.15. The rocky limestone scree slopes above were dominated by dog's mercury, and the heavy soils of the valley floors by the tufted hair grass, which grows in dense clumps and is a very strong competitor for the available space. Pigott and Taylor, on the basis of what was known about the preferred habitats of the stinging nettle, thought it likely that the plant required soils which were rich in nutrient elements, such as nitrogen and phosphorus. They made chemical analyses of the three main plant species occupying the valley and they found that the nettle contained more than twice as much nitrogen and over three times as much phosphorus as either

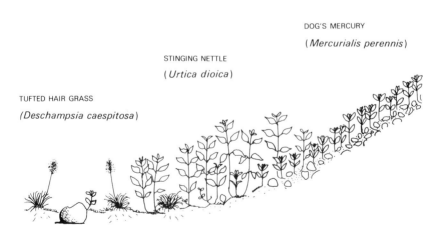

DOG'S MERCURY

(*Mercurialis perennis*)

STINGING NETTLE

(*Urtica dioica*)

TUFTED HAIR GRASS

(*Deschampsia caespitosa*)

Figure 1.15. Section of the floor of a valley in a limestone area of central England showing the distribution of the three major plant species present. (After Pigott and Taylor, 1964.[22])

of the other species. Therefore they confirmed that it is a very demanding plant.

Could it be that the failure of the nettle to dominate the upper slopes and the valley floor is due to a shortage of either or both of these elements in the soils? They tested this by growing nettles in soils from each of the three sites and adding either nitrogen (as ammonium nitrate), or phosphorus (as calcium phosphate) or both to some samples. They found that adding nitrogen alone did not stimulate nettle growth, so this could not have been in short supply. But the addition of phosphorus (with or without extra nitrogen) had a remarkable effect on the growth of the experimental nettles; the weights of individual nettle plants (after 50 days' growth) rose from an average of about 4 g to over 200 g in the case of soils from the *Deschampsia* and *Mercurialis* sites, and from about 50 g to 250 g in soils from the *Urtica* site. Phosphorus is, therefore, the most likely element to be restricting the success of the stinging nettle in this particular site.

Although few species have been worked upon as thoroughly as the stinging nettle, it is probable that the local distributions of many plants is influenced by soil factors in this way.

Influence of man   Man has had such a profound impact upon the face of the earth that very many species of plant and animal have had their distribution patterns modified by his activities. Some organisms have been brought into a close, almost symbiotic relationship with him as a result of the process of domestication. Others have had their ranges reduced by his destruction of their habitats; some, such as the passenger pigeon and the great auk, have become extinct.

Many more show the effects of man in their local distributions. The plantain is most common where man or his domesticated animals have disturbed soils by ploughing or trampling. The dragonflies and the woodland harvest spiders have both been affected by the destruction of their habitats. Many temperate forests are now fragmented into 'islands' between which alien, arable land presents a new barrier to dispersal. The horeshoe vetch and the Chalkhill blue butterfly have benefited from the maintenance of chalk and limestone grassland as a result of the grazing of domestic animals. The epiphytic lichens have suffered from the effects of woodland destruction and have also been subjected to the effects of air pollution to which they are particularly sensitive.

These, and many other ways in which man has been a potent force in modifying the distributions of organisms, will form the subject of Chapter 9.

References

1   NEAL E. (1948) *The Badger*. Penguin Books, Harmondsworth.
2   MARKS P.L. (1974) The role of the pin cherry (*Prunus pensylvanica* L.) in the maintenance of stability in northern hardwood ecosystems. *Ecol. Monogr.* **44**, 73–88.

3   PENNINGTON W. (1974) *The History of British Vegetation*. English Universities Press, London.

4   SHARROCK J.T.R. & SHARROCK E.M. (1976) *Rare Birds in Britain and Ireland*. T. and A.D. Poyser, Berkhamsted.

5   LOUSLEY J.E. (1970) The influence of transport on a changing flora. In: Perring F.H. (ed.), *The Flora of a Changing Britain*, pp. 73–83. E.W. Classey, Hampton.

6   SAGAR G.R. & HARPER J.L. (1964) Biological flora of the British Isles, *Plantago major* L., *P. media* L. and *P. lanceolata* L. *J. Ecol.* **52**, 189–221.

7   CORBET P.S., LONGFIELD C. & MOORE N.W. (1960) *Dragonflies*. New Naturalist Series, Collins, London.

8   CORBET P.S. (1957) The life history of the Emperor Dragonfly, *Anax imperator* Leach (Odonata: Aeshindae). *J. Anim. Ecol.* **26**,1–69.

9   CHAMBERLAIN C.J. (1919) *The Living Cycads*. University of Chicago Press, Chicago.

10 WHITING M.G. (1963) Toxicity of cycads. *Economic Botany* **17**, 271–302.

11 CASSAGNAU P. (1959) Contribution à la connaissance du genre *Tetracanthella* Schott. *Mem. Mus. nat. Hist. natur., Paris (Zool.)* **16** (7), 201–260.

12 SOUTHERN H.M., ed. (1977) *The Handbook of British Mammals*. Blackwell Scientific Publications, Oxford.

13 COOPE G.R. (1973) Tibetan species of dung beetle from Late Pleistocene deposits in England. *Nature, Lond.* **245**, 335–336.

14 FAVARGER C. (1972) Endemism in the montane floras of Europe. In: Valentine D.H. (ed.), *Taxonomy, Phytogeography and Evolution*, pp. 191–204. Academic Press, London.

15 MEYER E.R. (1973) Late Quaternary palaeoecology of the Cuatro Cienegas Basin, Coahuila, Mexico. *Ecology* **54**, 982–995.

16 LEWIS H. (1972) The origin of endemics in the California Flora. In: Valentine D.H. (ed.), *Taxonomy, Phytogeography and Evolution*, pp. 179–189. Academic Press, London.

17 TODD V. (1949) The habits and ecology of the British harvestmen (Arachnida, Opiliones) with special reference to those of the Oxford district. *J. Anim. Ecol.* **18**, 209–216.

18 ROSE F. (1974) The epiphytes of oak. In: Morris M.G. and Perring F.H. (eds), *The British Oak*, pp. 250–273. E.W. Classey, Hampton.

19 GEIGER R. (1955) *The Climate near the Ground*. Harvard University Press, Cambridge, Mass.

20 FORD E.B. (1945) *Butterflies*. New Naturalist Series, Collins, London.

21 ETHERINGTON J.R. (1975) *Environment and Plant Ecology*. John Wiley, London.

22 PIGOTT C.D. & TAYLOR K. (1964) The distribution of some woodland herbs in relation to the supply of nitrogen and phosphorus in the soil. *J. Ecol.* **52** (Jubilee Symp. Suppl.) 175–185.

CHAPTER 2

THE PHYSICAL LIMITATIONS OF LIFE

In Chapter 1, environmental conditions were often referred to as determining or limiting the distribution of plants and animals. It was suggested that these *limiting factors* in the environment include *physical factors* such as temperature, light, wetness, and dryness, as well as *biotic factors* such as competition, predation, or the presence or absence of suitable food. In this and in the following chapter the ways in which such factors influence organisms will be described in more detail.

First, though, the meaning of the term 'limiting factor' must be understood. Anything that tends to make it more difficult for a species to live, grow, or reproduce in its environment is a limiting factor for the species in that environment. To be limiting, such a factor need not necessarily be lethal for a species; it may simply make the working of its physiology or behaviour less efficient, so that it is less able to reproduce or to compete with other species for food or living space. For instance, we suggested in Chapter 1 that a northern limit may be set to the distribution of certain dragonflies by low night-time temperatures. In the more southerly parts of northern regions, at least, temperatures are not so low that they kill dragonflies *directly*, but they are low enough at night to force the insects to metamorphose during the day, when they are more vulnerable to predatory birds. In this case, then, the limiting factor of temperature does not operate directly but is connected with a biotic environmental factor, that of predation. Many other limiting factors act in a similar way.

Environmental gradients   Many physical and biotic factors affect any species of organism, but each can be considered as forming a *gradient*. For example, the physical factor of temperature affects species over a range from low temperatures at one extreme to high temperatures at the other, and this constitutes a temperature gradient. These gradients exist in all environments and affect all the species in each environment. As seen in Chapter 1, different species vary in their tolerance of environmental factors, being either *eurytopic* (ecologically tolerant) or *stenotopic* (ecologically intolerant), but each species can function efficiently over only a more or less limited part of each gradient. Within this *range of optimum*, the species can survive and maintain a large population; beyond it, toward both the low and the high ends of the gradient, the species suffers increasing physiological stress—it may stay alive, but because it cannot function efficiently, it can maintain only low populations. These areas of the gradient are bordered by the upper and lower limits of tolerance of the species to the environmental factor. Beyond these limits, the species cannot survive because conditions are too extreme; individuals may live there for short periods but will either die or pass quickly through to a more favourable area (Fig. 2.1).[1] A species may not achieve its full potential distribution in the field because of competitive interactions with other organisms. When under conditions of physiological stress, a species easily succumbs to such competition.

A relatively simple example of an environmental gradient is the global gradient in temperature which runs from hot equatorial regions northward to cold Arctic areas. The gradient has a great many local variations due to local climatic conditions, but in general there is a progression from hot to cold in average temperature through the year. The animals and plants adapted to live in cool-temperate conditions can obviously survive only in

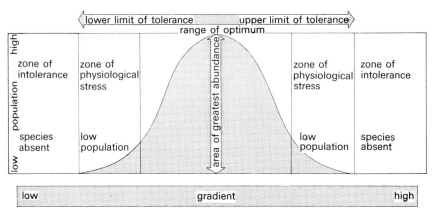

Figure 2.1. Graphical model of the population abundance maintained by a species of animal or plant along a gradient of a physical factor in its environment. (From Kendeigh, 1961.[1])

those parts of the global temperature gradient where such conditions are found. These cool-temperate regions, then, lie in the species' range of optimum, to the north of which lie areas that are too cold, and to the south of which lie regions that are too hot. In the southernmost parts of the cold end of the gradient, cool-temperate species may maintain low populations especially in favourable years, but further north these populations peter out as conditions become too cold. There will be similar areas with low populations in the northernmost regions of the warm end of the gradient.

The grey hair grass (*Corynephorus canescens*) is widespread in central and southern Europe and reaches its northern limit in the British Isles and southern Scandinavia (Fig. 2.2). J. K. Marshall has examined the factors which might be responsible for maintaining its northern limit, and he found that both flowering and germination were affected by low temperature.[2] The grass has a short life span (about 2–6 years), so it relies upon seed production to maintain its population. Any factor interfering with flowering or with germination could therefore limit its success in competi-

The Physical Limitations of Life

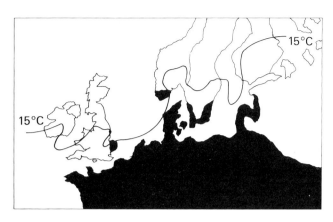

Figure 2.2. Distribution of the grey hair grass (*Corynephorus canescens*) in northern Europe (shaded) and its relationship to the 15°C July mean isotherm.

tive situations. At its northern limit, low summer temperature delays its flowering, with the result that the season is already well advanced when the seeds are shed. Seed germination is slowed down at temperatures below 15°C and seeds sown experimentally after October had a very poor survival rate. This may explain why its northern limit in Europe so closely matches the 15°C July mean isotherm.

Many plants have their seeds adapted to a specific temperature for germination and this often relates to conditions prevailing when germination is most appropriate for the species. P. A. Thompson of Kew Gardens, England, has devised a piece of apparatus for examining the effect of temperature on germination.[3] It consists of a metal bar, one end of which is maintained at −40°C and the other at 3°C; between is a gradient of temperatures. Groups of seeds of the species to be examined are placed along the bar and kept moist, and a record is kept of the number of days required for 50 per cent of the seeds within each group to germinate. The results are expressed on graphs, and the lowest point on the U-shaped curves shows the optimum temperature for germination.

In Figure 2.3 the germination responses of three members of the catchfly family are shown, together with their geographical ranges. The catchfly (*Silene secundiflora*) is a Mediterranean species, so the optimum time for germination is the autumn, when the hot, dry summer is over and the cool, moist winter is about to begin. Its optimum germination occurs at about 17°C. The ragged robin (*Lychnis flos-cuculi*) occurs throughout temperate Europe and here the cold winter is the least favourable for growth, hence there are advantages to be gained by germinating in the spring. Optimum germination occurs at about 27°C. The third species, the sticky catchfly (*Silene viscosa*), is an eastern European steppe species. The invasion of open grassland is an opportunistic business; each chance that offers itself must be taken, so any temperature limitation is likely to be an unacceptable restriction on a plant in its struggle for space. Wide tolerance

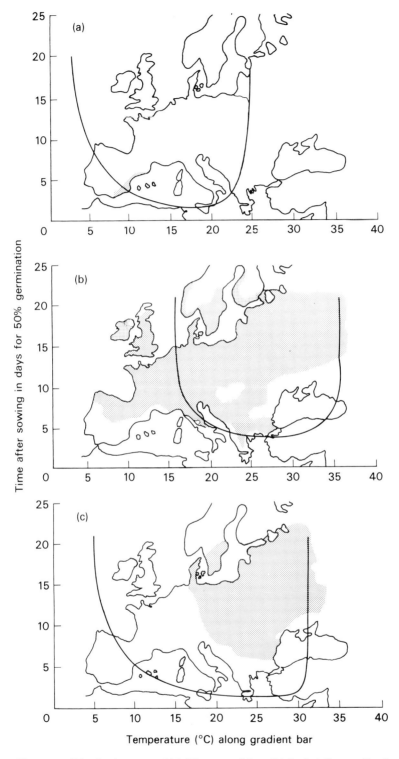

Figure 2.3. Distribution maps of (a) *Silene secundiflora*, (b) *Lychnis flos-cuculi* and (c) *Silene viscosa*, together with their germination responses to temperature. (After Thompson, 1970.[3])

of temperature is thus an advantage and *S. viscosa* seeds germinate well over the range $11-31°$C.

In most plants, the first product of photosynthesis is a sugar containing three carbon atoms; these plants are known as *C_3 plants*. In some plant species, however, there is a supplementary mechanism at work in which carbon dioxide is temporarily fixed into a four-carbon compound, later to be fed into the conventional fixation process in specialized cells around the bundles of conducting tissue in the leaf.[4] These *C_4 plants* occur in a number of different flowering plant families, mostly from tropical and subtropical regions. Some important tropical crop species, like sugar cane, are C_4 plants.

For a variety of biochemical reasons, the C_4 mechanism is most advantageous under conditions of high light intensity and high temperature, whereas it may be disadvantageous at low light and low temperature. J. R. Ehleringer has calculated that, at a latitude of about $45°$ in an area like the great plains of North America, the relative advantages and disadvantages of each system are roughly in balance (Fig. 2.4).[5] If one examines the proportion of C_3 and C_4 species among the grasses in different sites in North America, then one finds that the C_4 system occurs in more than 50 per cent of the grasses in most areas south of $40°$N and in less than 50 per cent north of that latitude (Fig. 2.5).[6] So competitive interaction between species of grass has led to the selection of the photosynthetic mechanism

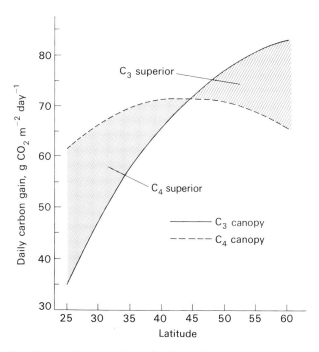

Figure 2.4. Predicted levels of photosynthesis for C_3 and C_4 species over a range of latitudes in the Great Plains during July. The C_4 advantage is lost in latitudes greater than $45°$C. (After Ehleringer, 1978.[5])

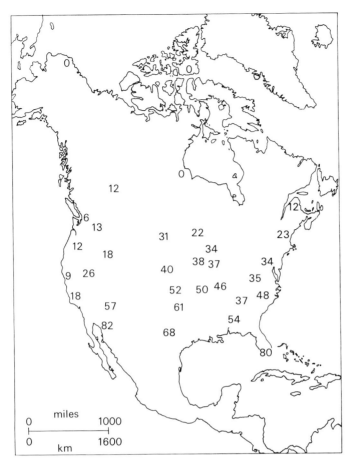

Figure 2.5. Proportion of C_4 species in the grass flora of various parts of North America. (After Teeri and Stowe, 1976.[6])

most appropriate to the needs of any given locality. Those C_4 species found north of the critical line are often associated with particular circumstances which favour them; for example, they may have their maximum growth rate in late summer when temperatures are highest, whilst the C_3 species grow best in the cooler conditions of spring and early summer.[7]

Although temperature is one of the most important environmental factors, because of its effect on the metabolic rate of organisms, many other physical factors in the environment are limiting ones. A whole family of factors is related to the amount of water present in the environment. Aquatic organisms obviously require water as the basic medium of their existence, but most terrestrial animals and plants, too, are limited by the wetness or dryness of the habitat, and often also by the humidity of the atmosphere, which in turn affects its 'drying power' (or more precisely, the rate of evaporation of water from the ground and from animals and plants). Light is of fundamental importance because it provides the energy that green plants fix into carbohydrates during photosynthesis, thus obtaining energy for themselves (and ultimately for all other organisms).

Light in its daily and seasonal fluctuation also regulates the activities of many animals. The concentrations of oxygen and carbon dioxide in the water or air surrounding organisms are also important. Oxygen is essential to most animals and plants for the release of energy from food by respiration, and carbon dioxide is vital because it is used as the raw material in the photosynthesis of carbohydrates by plants. Many other chemical factors of the environment are of importance, particularly soil chemistry where plants are concerned. Pressure is important to aquatic organisms; deep-sea animals are specially adapted to live at high pressures, but the tissues of species living in more shallow waters would be easily damaged by such pressures.

In marine environments, variation in the salinity of the water affects many organisms, because many marine organisms have body fluids with much the same salt concentration as sea water (about 35 parts per thousand), in which their body tissues are adapted to function efficiently. If they become immersed in a less saline medium (in estuaries, for instance), water moves into their tissues due to the physical process called *osmosis*, by which water passes from a dilute solution of a salt to a concentrated one. If the organisms cannot control the passage of water into their bodies, the body fluids are flooded and their tissues can no longer function. This problem of salinity is an important factor in preventing marine organisms from invading rivers, or freshwater ones from invading the sea and spreading across oceans to other continents (Fig. 2.6).

Interaction of factors   The environment of any species consists of an extremely complicated series of interacting gradients of all the factors, biotic as well as physical, and these influence its distribution and abundance. Populations of the species can live only in those areas where favourable parts of the environmental gradients that affect it overlap. Factors that fall outside this favourable region are limiting ones for the species in that environment.

Some of the interactions between the various factors in an organism's environment may be very complex and difficult for the ecologist to interpret or for the experimentalist to investigate. This is because a series of interacting factors may have more extreme effects on the behaviour and physiology of a species than any factor alone. To take a simple example, temperature and water interact strongly on organisms, because both high and low temperatures reduce the amout of water in an environment, high temperatures causing evaporation and low ones causing freezing, but it may be very hard to discover if an organism is being affected by heat or cold or by water lack. Similarly, light energy in the form of sunlight exerts a great influence on organisms because of its importance in photosynthesis and in vision, but it also has a heating effect on the atmosphere and on surfaces, and therefore raises temperatures. In natural situations it is often

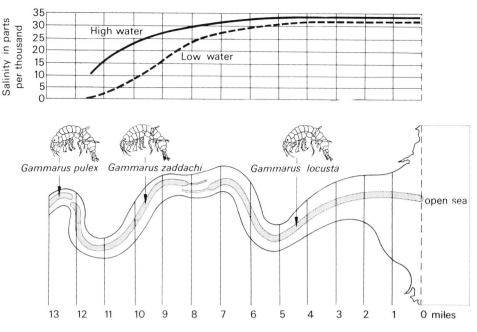

Figure 2.6. The distribution along a river of three closely related species of amphipod (Crustacea), relative to the concentration of salt in the water. *Gammarus locusta* is an estuarine species and is found in regions where salt concentration does not fall below about 25 parts per thousand. *G. zaddachi* is a species with a moderate tolerance of salt water and is found along a stretch of water between 8 and 12 miles from the river mouth where salt concentrations average 10–20 parts per thousand. *G. pulex* is a true freshwater species and does not occur at all in parts of the river showing any influence of the tide or salt water.[8]

almost impossible to tell which of many possible limiting factors is mainly responsible for the distribution of a particular species.

An interesting example of the complexity of interaction between environmental factors was studied by the American ecologist M. R. Warburg, in his work on two species of woodlice (sowbugs or slaters, Crustacea, Isopoda) living in rather dry habitats in southern Arizona.[9, 10] One species, *Armadillidium vulgare*, is found mostly in grasslands and scrubby woodland and is also widely distributed in similar habitats elsewhere in North America and in Europe. The other, *Venezilla arizonicus*, is a rather rare species, confined to the south-western United States and found in very arid country, with stony soil and a sparse vegetation of cactus and acacia. Warburg investigated the reactions of these two species to three environmental factors: temperature, atmospheric humidity and light. His experimental techniques involved the use of a simple apparatus, the choice chamber or *preferendum apparatus*, in which animals may be placed in a controlled gradient of an environmental factor. The behaviour of the animals, particularly the direction in which they move and their speed, can then be used to suggest which part of the gradient they find most satisfactory; this is termed the preferendum of

The Physical Limitations of Life

these particular animals in this particular gradient. Warburg's method for testing the interactions of light, temperature and humidity on the woodlice was the classic scientific approach of isolating the effects of each factor separately, and then testing them two or three at a time in all possible combinations. For instance, he might set up a gradient of temperature between hot and cold and test the reactions of the animals to this, either with the whole gradient at a low humidity (dry) or the whole gradient at a high humidity (wet), or with the hot end of the gradient dry and the cold wet, or with the cold end dry and the hot end wet. He might then test the effect of light on these four situations by exposing each in turn to constant illumination, constant darkness, or one end of the gradient in darkness and the other in light. Such work is extremely time-consuming and requires great patience.

Warburg found that, in general, *A. vulgare* prefers low temperatures (around 10–15°C), high humidities (above 70 per cent relative humidity, i.e. the air is 70 per cent saturated with water vapour) and is rather weakly attracted to light. This accords well with what is known of the species' habitat and habits—it lives in fairly humid, cool places and is active during the day. *Venezilla arizonicus*, on the other hand, prefers lower humidities (around 45 per cent), higher temperatures (20–25°C) and will generally move away from the light. Again, this accords well with the species' habits, since it lives in rather dry, warm places and is active at night. The reactions of the species change, however, and become harder to interpret when they are exposed to more extreme conditions. For instance, at high temperatures (35–40°C), *Armadillidium vulgare* tends to choose lower humidities, irrespective of whether these were in light or dark. One of several possible explanations for this behaviour is that, at these high temperatures, the species' physiological processes can be maintained only if body temperatures are lowered by permitting loss of water vapour from the body surface, which is more rapid at lower humidities. The normal reaction of *Venezilla arizonicus* changes if the species is exposed to very high humidities; it then tends to move to dryer conditions even if these are in the light. Warburg concludes that, for these two species, light is not really an important physiological factor and acts mostly as a 'token stimulus', a clue to where optimum conditions of humidity and temperature may be found. For *V. arizonicus*, which lives in a dry or *xeric* habitat, darkness indicates the likely presence of the high temperatures and low humidities it prefers. For *Armadillidium vulgare*, in its cooler, more humid or *mesic* habitat, there is little risk of desiccation except in the most exposed situations and the species can afford to be relatively indifferent to light.

Warburg's study indicates the great complexity of the reactions of even relatively simple invertebrate animals such as Crustacea to the physical factors of their environment. If we analyse also the biotic factors of the animal's environment, food and enemies, the picture becomes even more complex. Other studies of *A. vulgare*, for instance, in California, indicate that the species shows quite strong preferences for different types of food (mostly various types of dead vegetation) and these also influence its distribution.[11]

Patterns of climate Many of the most important physical factors of the land environment have very distinct patterns of variation in different parts of the world. This pattern we call *climate*. The climate of an area is the whole range of weather conditions, temperature, rainfall, evaporation, water, sunlight and wind that it experiences through all the seasons of the year. Many factors are involved in the determination of the climate of an area, particularly latitude, altitude, and position in relation to seas and land-masses. The climate in turn largely determines the species of plants and animals that can live in an area.[12]

Climate varies with latitude for two reasons. The first reason is that the spherical form of the earth results in an uneven distribution of solar energy with respect to latitude, as shown in Figure 2.7a. As the angle of incidence of the sun's rays approaches 90°, the area over which the energy is spread is reduced, so that there is an increased heating effect. In the high latitudes, energy is spread over a wide area; thus polar climates are cold. The precise latitude that receives sunlight at 90° at noon varies during the year; it is at the Equator during March and September, at the Tropic of Cancer (23·45°N) during June, and at the Tropic of Capricorn (23·45°S) during December. The effect of this seasonal fluctuation is more profound in some regions than in others.

The second reason is that variations also result from the pattern of movement of air masses. Figure 2.7b shows an idealized picture which assumes a uniform surface to the Earth. Under these conditions air is heated over the Equator, and therefore rises (causing a low pressure area) and moves towards the pole. As it moves towards the pole, it gradually cools and increases in density until it descends, where it forms a subtropical region of high pressure, known as the Horse Latitudes. Air from this high pressure area either moves towards the Equator, or else moves polewards. This latter air eventually meets cold air currents moving south from the polar region, over which air is cooled and descending (causing a high pressure area). Where these two air masses meet, a region of unstable low pressure results, in which the weather is changeable.[13]

This idealized picture is complicated by the *Coriolis effect* (named in honour of the French mathematician Gaspard Coriolis, who analysed it), which results from the east–west rotation of the Earth. This force tends to deflect a moving object to the right of its course in the Northern Hemisphere and to the left in the Southern Hemisphere (Fig. 2.7c). As a result, the winds moving towards the Equator come to blow from a more easterly direction. These 'Trade Winds', coming from both the Northern and the Southern Hemispheres, therefore meet at the Equator, and this region is known as the 'inter-tropical convergence'. Where these easterly winds have passed over oceans they have become moist, and this moisture is deposited as rain over the easterly portions of the equatorial latitudes of the continents. Similarly, the winds which move polewards from the high pressure Horse Latitudes come to blow from a more westerly direction, and provide rain along the westerly regions of the higher latitudes of the continents. The Horse Latitudes themselves are regions in which dry air is descending, and arid belts form along these latitudes of the continents.

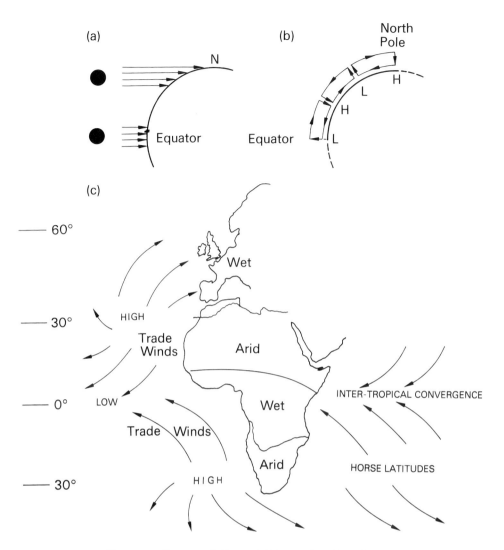

Figure 2.7. Patterns of climate. (a) Due to the spherical shape of the earth polar regions receive less solar energy per unit area than the equatorial regions. (b) The major patterns of circulating air masses (cells) in the Northern Hemisphere: H, high pressure; L, low pressure. (c) Pressure areas, wind directions, and moisture belts around Europe and Africa.

The distribution of oceans and land-masses modifies this simple picture yet further. Because heat is gained or released more slowly by water than by land-masses, heat exchange is slower in maritime regions, while at the same time humidities are higher. In summer, therefore, continental areas tend to develop low-pressure systems as a result of the heating of land-masses and the conduction of this heat to the overlying air masses. Conversely, in winter the reverse situation occurs, continental areas becoming cold faster than the oceans, and high pressure systems developing over them. Because most of the Earth's land areas occur in the Northern Hemisphere, the ideal situation shown in the diagram is disrupted to a far greater extent in the Northern than in the Southern Hemisphere.

In addition to the heating and cooling effects of land-masses, climate is also affected by altitude. On average, the air temperature falls by 0·6°C for every 100-m rise in height, but this varies considerably according to prevailing conditions, especially the aspect and steepness of slope and the wind exposure. Because of this tendency for temperature to fall with increasing altitude, the organisms inhabiting high tropical and subtropical mountains—such as the Himalayas in northern India (Fig. 2.8)—may be

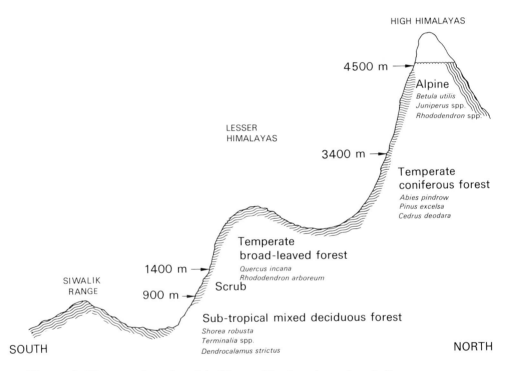

HIGH HIMALAYAS

4500 m →

Alpine
Betula utilis
Juniperus spp.
Rhododendron spp.

LESSER
HIMALAYAS

3400 m →

Temperate
coniferous forest
Abies pindrow
Pinus excelsa
Cedrus deodara

Temperate
broad-leaved forest
1400 m → *Quercus incana*
Rhododendron arboreum
900 m → Scrub

SIWALIK
RANGE

Sub-tropical mixed deciduous forest
Shorea robusta
Terminalia spp.
Dendrocalamus strictus

SOUTH

NORTH

Figure 2.8. Diagrammatic section of the Western Himalayas in northern India showing the approximate altitudinal limits of the major vegetation types. The scrub zone (900–1400 m) is strongly modified by the activities of man.

more like the flora and fauna of colder regions than that of the surrounding lowlands.[14] However, although temperature in general falls as one ascends such mountains, other environmental conditions do not precisely mirror those found at higher latitudes. For example, the seasonal variations in day-length typical of high latitude tundra areas are not found in the 'alpine' regions of tropical mountains. Also the high degree of insolation resulting from the high angle of the sun produces considerable diurnal fluctuations in temperature that are not found in tundra regions. It is not

The Physical Limitations of Life

surprising, therefore, that the altitudinal zonation of plants and animals should not precisely reflect the global, latitudinal zonation. Also, arctic and alpine races of a single species often differ in their physiological make-up as a consequence of these climatic differences.

Day-length and latitude   The length of days and nights varies with season, and the most marked variations are found at high latitudes. Because of this, animals and plants have evolved mechanisms for the detection of the length of light and dark periods and can use them as triggers for the commencement of various processes, such as breeding, migration, or flowering. Such a response to light and dark is called *photoperiodism*.

One plant which has been extensively studied in this respect is the cocklebur (*Xanthium strumarium*).[15] This is a widespread weed in many parts of the world, often having been carried and introduced accidentally by man, as in India and Hawaii. It requires a critical length of darkness before it is able to flower; as days become longer in the spring there comes a point when the critical night-length is reached and flowering begins. Since day-length varies with latitude one would expect the night-length requirement also to vary, and this is indeed the case. Figure 2.9 shows the night-length requirement of the cocklebur in various parts of the United

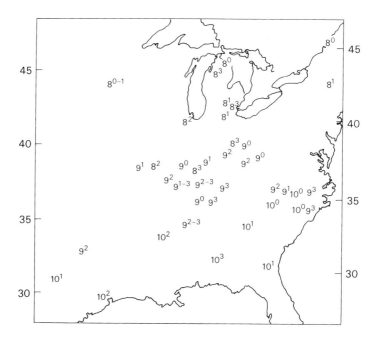

Figure 2.9. The night-length requirements of populations of the cocklebur (*Xanthium strumarium*) from various sites in eastern North America. Superscripts refer to additional units of quarter of an hour, e.g. $9^1 = 9$ h 15 min, $9^2 = 9$ h 30 min, etc. (After Ray and Alexander, 1966.[15])

States. It can be seen that in the Great Lakes region flowering begins when the night-length falls to about 8 h, whereas in Texas it commences at 10 h. A gradient is even found within the state of Texas (Fig. 2.10).[16]

An interesting feature of the adaptation is that it remains unchanged (over fairly short periods of time) when plants are moved from one part of the world to another (as in the case of the strawberry tree, p. 18). This fact has allowed Calvin McMillan of the University of Texas to carry out some interesting detective work on the origins of cocklebur populations which have been introduced into various parts of the world.[17] For example, the cockleburs of Hawaii were believed to have originated in California, but

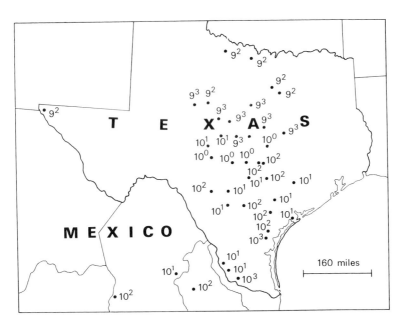

Figure 2.10. Variation in the night-length requirement of the cocklebur (*Xanthium strumarium*) within Texas and north-east Mexico. Times are expressed as in Figure 2.9. (After McMillan, 1970.[17])

the native cockleburs of that state vary in their night-length requirement from 8 h in the north to 9·5 h in the south, whereas the Hawaiian plants were found to need about 11 h for flowering. This implies that they originated well to the south of California, probably from Mexico.

If day-length is to be a useful trigger for a biological process, such as growth or reproduction, it must be tuned to variations in altitude as well as latitude. At high altitude one would expect the photoperiodic response to be delayed so that breeding or flowering would not commence until later in the season. W. E. Bradshaw has examined this in a mosquito, *Wyeomyia smithii*.[18] This is an extraordinary animal because it inhabits the pitcher-like leaves of the insectivorous pitcher plant, *Sarracenia purpurea*. It spends the winter as a dormant larva within the pools of digestive juices in the hollow leaves. This dormancy, or *diapause*, is terminated as days grow longer in the spring, and the critical photoperiod is found to be closely correlated with latitude, varying between 12 h and 16 h over 19° of latitude in North America. Its photoperiod is also correlated with altitude. Figure 2.11 shows the relationship between the day-length required for growth commencement and the length of the growing season (number of frost-free days). The length of the growing season is, of course, itself closely related to both latitude and altitude. It appears that the growth time-switch in the pitcher plant mosquito is delicately tuned, through evolutionary selection, to promote development at the best possible time of year.

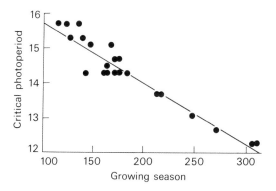

Figure 2.11. Relationship between day-length requirement and growing season (number of frost-free days per year) for the termination of diapause in the pitcher-plant mosquito (*Wyeomyia smithii*). (After Bradshaw, 1976.[18])

Climatic zones The climate of an area is the result of the many varying factors that affect the region, and the Earth's surface accordingly experiences a great variety of climates distributed over it in an intricate pattern; they can be classified into five divisions, though each contains scores of regional variants. These are shown in Figure 2.12.

As we have seen, plants and animals are affected by a whole range of physical factors in their environment, many of these being directly related to climate. Biogeographers have long sought, therefore, a means of portraying climates in simple, condensed form which would give at a glance an indication of the main features which might be of critical importance to the organisms of the area. Mean values of temperature and rainfall may be of some use, but one also needs to know something of seasonal variation and of extreme values if the full implications of a particular climatic regime are to be appreciated. It is with this aim in view that Heinrich Walter of the University of Hohenheim in West Germany devised a form of climate diagram which is now widely used by biogeographers.[19,20] An explanation of the form of these diagrams is given in Figure 2.13 and they are used later in this chapter when the major biological zones of the earth are described.

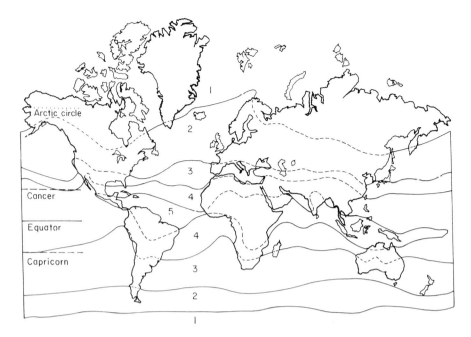

Figure 2.12. A simple classification of climates into five major types and their distribution on the surface of the earth. Key: 1, cold; 2, cold-temperate; 3, warm-temperate; 4, subtropical; 5, tropical.

Biomes and life-forms   Each of these climatic types and their major subdivisions has a number of characteristic plant and animal communities that have evolved so that they are well adapted to the range of environmental factors in them; such characteristic communities are called *biomes*. The distinctions between biomes are not necessarily related to the taxonomic classification of the organisms they contain, but rather to the *life-form* (the form, structure, habits and type of life-history of the organism in response to its environment) of their plants and animals. This concept of the life-form was first put forward by the Danish botanist Christen Raunkaier in 1903.[21] He observed that the most common or dominant types of plants in a climatic region had a form well suited to survive in the prevailing conditions.

Thus in arctic conditions, the most common plants are dwarf shrubs and cushion-forming species which have their buds close to ground level. In this way they survive the winter conditions when wind-borne ice particles would have an abrasive effect on any elevated shoots. In warmer climates, buds may be carried well above the ground and the tree is an efficient life-form, but periodic cold or drought may necessitate the loss of foliage and the development of a dormant phase. This has resulted in the evolution of the deciduous habit. Prolonged drought is again associated with shrubs which have smaller above-ground structures. Some plants of areas with seasonal drought survive the unfavourable period as underground perennating organs (bulbs or corms) or as dormant seeds.

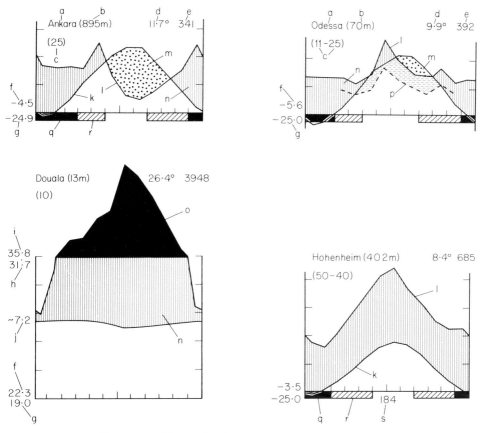

Figure 2.13. Key to the climatic diagrams. Abscissa: months (N. Hemisphere January–December, S. Hemisphere July–June); Ordinate: one division = 10 °C or 20 mm rain. a = station, b = height above sea-level, c = duration of observations in years (of two figures the first indicates temperature, the second precipitation), d = mean annual temperature in °C, e = mean annual precipitation in mm, f = mean daily minimum of the coldest month, g = lowest temperature recorded, h = mean daily maximum of the warmest month, i = highest temperature recorded, j = mean daily temperature variations, k = curve of mean monthly temperature, l = curve of mean monthly precipitation, m = relative period of drought (dotted), n = relative humid season (vertical shading), o = mean monthly rain > 100 mm (black scale reduced to 1/10), p = reduced supplementary precipitation curve (10°C = 30 mm) and above it (dashes) dry period, q = months with mean daily minimum below 0°C (diagonal shading) = late or early frosts occur, s = mean duration of frost-free period in days. Some values are missing, where no data are available for the stations concerned (h–j are only given for diurnal types of climate). (After Walter, 1979.[20])

Animals, too, show distinct life-forms adapted to different climates, with cold-resistant, seasonal, or hibernating forms in cold regions and forms with drought-resistant skins or cuticles in deserts. Nevertheless, animal life-forms are usually far less easy to recognize than are those of plants and, consequently, most biomes are distinguished by the plants they contain and are named after their dominant plant life-form.

Since the energy-rich compounds which are built up by green plants form the basis of energy supply to all organisms, it is valuable to know how productive various parts of the world are. Figure 2.14 shows a map constructed by H. Lieth displaying the world distribution of potential plant productivity. It can be seen that the most productive parts of the globe are those areas currently occupied by tropical forests (compare with Fig. 2.16). This is discussed further in Chapter 3 (p. 70).

There is no real agreement among biogeographers about the number of biomes in the world. This is because it is often difficult to tell whether a

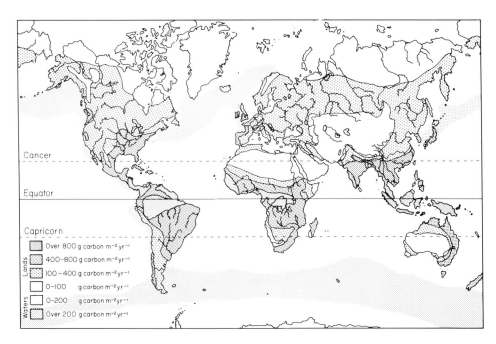

Figure 2.14. World distribution of plant productivity. this estimates the amount of organic dry matter which accumulates during a single growing season. Full adjustment for the losses due to animal consumption and deposition has not been made. Map compiled by H. Lieth.

particular type of vegetation is really a distinct form or is merely an early stage of development of another, and also because many types of vegetation have been much modified by the activities of man.

We shall describe eight terrestrial biomes, a freshwater one, and three marine ones. Figure 2.15 shows the way in which these biomes are related to climatic factors and Figure 2.16 shows their geographical distributions.

Tundra (Fig. 2.17) is found around the Arctic Circle, north of the tree-line. Smaller areas occur in the Southern Hemisphere on sub-Antarctic islands. Alpine tundra occurs above the tree-line on high mountains, including those in the tropics. It is the most continuous of biomes and the easiest to

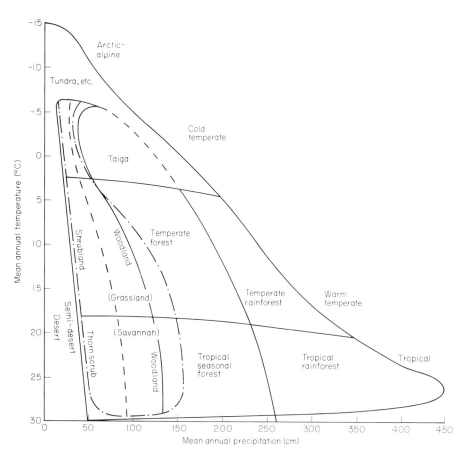

Figure 2.15. The distribution of the major terrestrial biomes with respect to mean annual precipitation and mean annual temperature. Within regions delimited by the dashed line a number of factors, including oceanicity, seasonality of drought, and human land-use may affect the biome type which develops. (From Whittaker, 1975.[26])

define. Winter temperatures may be as low as − 57 c: water melts at the soil surface in summer (air temperature is rarely over 15 c) but there is always a permanent layer of frozen soil underneath—the *permafrost*. There is a very short growing season, and only cold-tolerant plants can survive (Fig. 2.23). Typical plants are mosses, lichens, sedges, and dwarf trees. Large herbivores include reindeer, caribou and musk ox. Small herbivores include snow-shoe hares, lemmings and voles. Many birds migrate there from the south in summer, feeding on the large insect populations in the tundra during that season. Carnivores are Arctic fox, wolves, hawks, falcons and owls.

Northern Coniferous Forest (Taiga) (Fig. 2.18) forms an almost unbroken belt across the whole of northern North America and Eurasia, and is one of the most extensive biomes. Its northern margin with the tundra often has

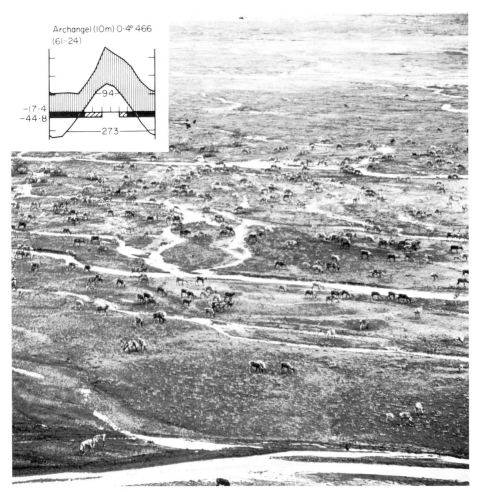

Archangel (10m) 0·4° 466
(61-24)

9·4

-17·4
-44·8

273

Figure 2.17. Tundra with caribou; interior of Alaska, Mt McKinley Park. Inset shows a climate diagram for tundra (Archangel, Alaska), see Figure 2.13 for explanation.

and broad-leaf deciduous trees. This was the original climax vegetation of much of north-central Europe, eastern Asia, and north-east North America; little remains today. (2) Mixed forests of conifers and broad-leaf evergreens. This once covered much of the Mediterranean lands but very little is left. It still occurs in the Southern Hemisphere, in Chile, New Zealand, Tasmania and South Africa (see Fig. 2.23). (3) Broad-leaf forests almost entirely of deciduous trees. This formerly covered much of Europe, northern Asia and eastern North America, and is found in the Southern Hemisphere only in Patagonia. (4) The rare broad-leaf forest consisting almost entirely of evergreens. This occurs throughout much of Florida, and also in north-east Mexico and in Japan. In the Southern Hemisphere it occurs on the southern tip of South Island, New Zealand. All these regions have very high rainfall, and the dripping forests have

Verkhoyansk (122m)−16·1° 128
(37−31)

−70·0

74

170

Figure 2.18. Northern coniferous forest area; Canadian Rocky Mountains. Inset shows a climate diagram for the taiga (Verkhoyansk, Siberia).

been termed 'temperate rain-forests'. In all temperate forests, there is frequently an understorey of saplings, shrubs and tall herbs, which is particularly well developed near the forest edge or where human interference has occurred. Temperate forests have warm summers but cold winters, except on western seaboards. Winter temperatures may fall below freezing-point. The deciduous trees escape these cold winters by losing their leaves; many plants have underground over-wintering organs. The fauna includes bears, wild boar, badgers, squirrels, woodchucks, many insectivores and rodents. Predators include wolves and wild cats (on the decline), red foxes and owls. Large herbivores are the deer. This biome is extremely rich in bird species, especially woodpeckers, titmice, thrushes, warblers and finches.

Washington D.C. (22m) 13·8°1053
(30)
-1·7
-26·1

Figure 2.19. Temperate forest; West Germany. Inset shows a climate diagram for the temperate deciduous forest biome (Washington D.C., USA).

Tropical rain-forest (Fig. 2.20) occurs between the Tropics of Cancer and Capricorn in areas where temperatures and light intensity are always high and rainfall is greater than 200 cm a year (and is at least 12 cm in the driest month). There is a great variety of trees (see p. 95): in some parts of the Brazilian rain-forests, there are as many as 300 species of trees in 2 km². The popular image of the jungle—thick, steamy and impenetrable—is borne out only in those areas that man has at some time cleared, especially along river margins; true climax tropical forest has very little under-growth. The canopy is extremely dense; the light intensity below may be as low as 1 per cent of that above, and thus only a few extremely shade-tolerant plants can survive there. Life is concentrated in the canopy, where there is plenty of light. The crowns of the trees are covered with *epiphytes*—plants that use the trees only for support and are not parasites.

Figure 2.20. Tropical rain forest biome; Puerto Rico. Inset shows a climate diagram from the tropical forest biome (Colombo, Sri Lanka).

Lianas—vines rooted in the ground but with leaves and flowers in the canopy—are also characteristic. Dead plants are rapidly decomposed, so there is little undecayed plant matter on the forest floor. The rate of turnover of nutrients is very high and the tropical forest has a higher productivity than that of any other terrestrial biome. The tropical rain forest biome contains the greatest variety of animal life of any biome, because of the richness of the food resources that it offers and the relative constancy of the conditions of the environment through the year. There is a great profusion of birds with many different diets—seeds, fruit, buds, nectar, or insects. Many of the mammals are adapted to arboreal life (monkeys, sloths, ant-eaters, many small carnivores) but there are also many ground-living forms, including rodents, deer and peccaries. Amphibia, and reptiles, especially snakes, are important as predators of small vertebrates and invertebrates.

Temperate grassland (Fig. 2.23) occurs in regions where rainfall is intermediate between those of desert and of temperate forest, and where there is a fairly long dry season. Temperate grassland has many local names—the *prairies* of North America, the *steppes* of Eurasia, the *pampas* of South America, and the *veld* of South Africa—but the dominant plants in all of them are the grasses, the most widespread and successful group of land plants. The soil always contains a thick layer of humus, unlike some forest soils, but is more exposed than the latter, and therefore more likely to dry out. The dominant animals are large grazing mammals—on the North American prairies, vast herds of bison and prong-horn (which man had virtually wiped out by the close of the last century, but is now reintroducing); over the steppes of Eurasia, the saiga antelope, wild horse and wild ass once roamed in herds; in the South American pampas, the natural grazer is the guanaco; and in Australia, the kangaroos fill this role. All these have been largely replaced by man with domestic grazing animals, often with disastrous results, as we shall see in Chapter 9, although grasses are adapted to withstand the effects of natural grazing.

Tropical grassland or savannah (Fig. 2.21) is a term applied to any tropical vegetation ranging from pure grassland to woodland with much grass. It covers a wide belt on either side of the Equator between the Tropics of Cancer and Capricorn. The climate is always very warm and there is a long dry season, and thus the plants often have drought-resisting features. The grass is much longer than that of temperate grassland, growing to 3·5 m. There is often a great variety of trees, which also show drought-resisting features; a typical group is the acacias. The dominant animals are large grazing mammals, the African savannah having the greatest variety, and burrowing rodents are also found. Large carnivores, such as lions and hyaenas, prey on the grazers.

Chaparral (Fig. 2.23) occurs where there are mild wet winters and pronounced summer droughts (known as Mediterranean climate), and in areas with less rain than grasslands. The vegetation is *sclerophyllous* (hard-leaf) scrub of low-growing woody plants, mainly evergreen with hard, thick, waxy leaves—adaptations to drought. In the Northern Hemisphere it occurs mainly in countries fringing the Mediterranean basin, but also in north-west Mexico and California. Formerly this biome had a varied flora and fauna, with many herbivores such as ground squirrels, deer and elk, and mountain lions and wolves as their predators, but this has been greatly reduced by man. In the Southern Hemisphere there are small areas of chaparral in southern Australia, southern Chile, and South Africa.

Deserts (Fig. 2.22) are areas experiencing extreme drought. A good definition is those areas where rainfall is less than 25 cm per year, or—if higher—is mostly lost immediately by evaporation. Deserts can be divided into hot deserts (such as the Sahara) with very high daytime temperatures, often over 50 C, and low night-time temperatures below

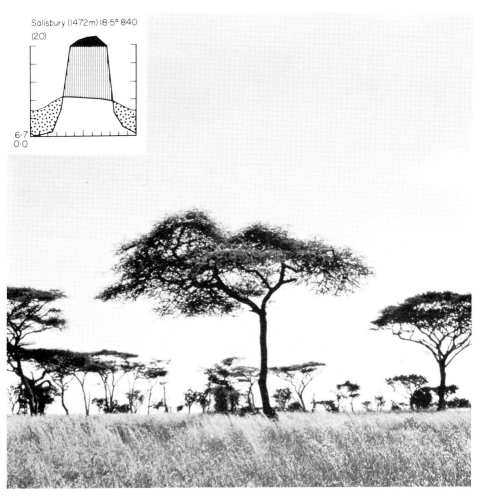

Figure 2.21. Savannah biome; Kenya. Inset shows a climate diagram for the tropical grassland biome (Salisbury, Zimbabwe Rhodesia).

20°C with relatively mild winters, and cold deserts (such as the Gobi Desert in Mongolia) with very severe winters and long periods of extreme cold (Fig. 2.23). Typical desert has large areas of barren rock or sand and very sparse vegetation. Desert plants are adapted to drought in various ways: some have drought-resistant seeds; others have small thick leaves that are shed in dry periods; yet others, such as the New World cacti, are succulents, storing water in their stems. Desert animals are mostly small enough to hide under stones or in burrows during the intense daytime heat in hot deserts. Certain rodents are well adapted to desert life—they live in cool burrows, are largely nocturnal, and waste very little water in their urine. Insects and reptiles lose little water, having waterproof skins and excreting almost dry, crystalline urine. Deserts spread when wind carries the top sand away, or when man encourages his domestic animals to overgraze their edges.

Chapter 2 57

Baghdad (34m) 22·6° 140

(15)

4·0
−7·7

Figure 2.22. Desert biome; Argentina. Inset shows a climate diagram from a semi-arid region (Baghdad, Iraq).

Freshwater biomes are far less self-contained than those of the surrounding land or the open sea. They receive a continual supply of nutrients from the land, but much of this is washed downstream in the rivers and there is an overall loss of organic material. Thus they are generally far less rich in nutrients than oceans, and usually less productive than either sea or land environments. They are more changeable than ocean or land biomes; rivers gradually wear away the land through which they pass and thus the river biome itself gradually changes, and many small ponds are seasonal, drying up in summer. There is a wide range of freshwater environments, from small ponds and streams to vast lakes and wide rivers. At the lower end of the scale, they are often better considered merely as a wet extension of the surrounding terrestrial biome. The dominant plants of larger lakes and slow rivers are phytoplankton, but larger floating and rooted plants cover considerable areas. Many of the animals are restricted to the freshwater habitat; amphibians, though living on land, need fresh water in which to breed; land animals use fresh water for drinking and bathing; and many birds are adapted to the freshwater habitats. Animal communities in large lakes correspond to planktonic, nektonic and benthic communities of the oceanic biome (see below). Some large lakes have well-defined shores, constituting sub-biomes: examples are the Great Lakes with their dune systems, or Lake Victoria with its muddy shores. Marshes (salt marshes and freshwater mires) are best considered as intermediate between marine or freshwater biomes and the surrounding terrestrial biome, and estuaries are transitional both between freshwater and marine biomes and also

The Physical Limitations of Life

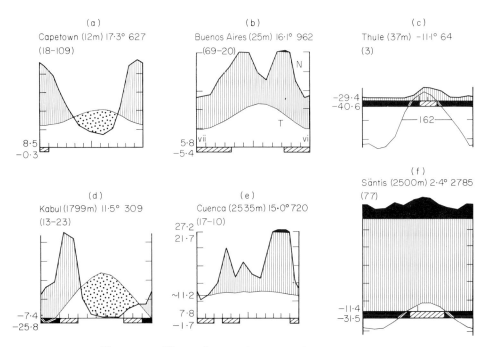

Figure 2.23. Climate diagrams from some other sites: (a) Capetown, South Africa; Mediterranean climate with winter rain and summer drought; chaparral. (b) Buenos Aires, Argentina; warm temperate climate with wet, evergreen forest. (c) Thule, Iceland; tundra. (d) Kabul, Afghanistan; steppe with cold winter and hot, dry summer. (e) Cuenca, Ecuador; mountain climate. (f) Säntis, Switzerland; mountain climate with high precipitation. Refer to Figure 2.13 for explanation.

between the water and the land. They have a very complex structure and are highly productive, with a great variety of plant and animal life. Freshwater habitats have suffered greatly from pollution by man—toxic industrial wastes, detergents, and vast quantities of sewage are dumped into rivers and lakes, and cause the extinction of all but a few resistant forms of life.

Marine biomes Land covers only 29 per cent of the earth's surface, whereas the oceans take up 71 per cent, with an average depth of 3900 metres. It is impossible to distinguish regional biomes in the seas, because of the uniformity of the marine environment and of the ease of distribution of its inhabitants. On the land, animals and plants of different latitudes have different life-forms; in the sea, animals do have distinctive forms, but these vary according to the depth at which they live, rather than according to latitude—for example, deep-sea animals are of a life-form especially adapted to cope with high pressures and total darkness. Water has a higher specific heat than soil or rock, and even the warmest oceans never reach the high temperatures of tropical forests or hot deserts. Similarly, the coldest seas are never as cold as the tundra or northern forests. The surface temperature is never greater than 30°C and rarely falls below 0°C. Marine organisms obviously have no problems in obtaining sufficient water, but light is a limiting factor. The tiny photosynthetic plants (*phytoplankton*) are restricted to the upper photic zone (the uppermost 200 m); virtually no light penetrates below 500 m. Atmospheric oxygen and carbon dioxide are plentiful at the surface and these gases are also dissolved in the water. Pressure is an important factor limiting the downward movement of shallow-water species. Sea water is much richer in nutrients than fresh water, and these are recycled to the photic zone by upwellings of deep currents. In some other areas, surface waters converge and descend. Where these are already exhausted of nutrients, the area of descent forms a 'desert', such as the Sargasso Sea in the southern North Atlantic. Such areas are the only virtually unproductive parts of the surface waters.

There are three principal marine biomes. (1) The *oceanic biome* of open water,[22] away from the immediate influence of the shore. This is further divided into the *planktonic sub-biome* containing free-floating plankton (mostly microscopic organisms with buoyancy mechanisms); the *nektonic sub-biome* of active swimmers, including fish, squids, turtles and marine mammals; and the *benthic sub-biome*, whose fauna is especially adapted for life on the sea-floor. (2) The *rocky shore biome*[23] is dominated by large brown seaweeds. These show a distinct pattern of zonation up the shore (see Fig. 2.24) as a response to the increasingly long period of desiccation which is experienced as one moves upwards from the low-water mark. Benthic animals display a similar zonation (see Fig. 3.13). (3) The *muddy* or *sandy shore biome*[24] is constantly receiving a supply of mud or sand which accumulates and forms an unstable substrate for attachment. Few algae can survive (for example the sea lettuce, *Ulva*), but many animals, such as burrowing worms, bivalve molluscs and crustaceans, live in the sediment. These are preyed upon by wading birds.

Soil It is evident that soils influence the distribution of certain plant species, but what is less evident is that vegetation interacts with climate to influence the development of soil. Soil consists of a very complex mixture of fragments of mineral material of various sizes, derived from the physical and chemical breakdown or *weathering* of the underlying rock.[25] Within this matrix of particles are found the organic products of decomposing plant and animal remains, together with water and air, which permeate the soil pores. In the course of time, as water moves through the soil, this organic matter can influence the distribution of chemicals in the soil profile, particularly if the overall direction of water movement is downwards. The result is the formation of a series of layers, or *horizons*, which characterize the soil profile. These horizons are often given the letters A, B, C and D, which are sometimes subdivided yet further. The A horizon is one which has lost soluble material as a result of downward water movement (leaching). It is said to be *eluviated*. It may be divided into Aoo and Ao horizons, which consist of organic litter in the course of decay, A1 horizon in which organic and mineral matter is intermixed, and A2 horizon which is often bleached white as a result of the loss both of organic matter and of iron and aluminium oxides. In the B horizon these are

Figure 2.24. Zonation of seaweed on a sheltered rocky shore; South Devon, England, seashore. Top: *Pelvetia canaliculata* (Channelled wrack). Middle: *Fucus spiralis* (Spiral wrack). Bottom: *Ascophyllum nodosum* (Knotted wrack).

redeposited (*illuviated* horizon)—organic matter mainly in the B1 horizon and iron and aluminium in the B2 horizon. The C horizon is unleached and consists of weathering fragments of the parent rock, whilst the D horizon is the parent rock itself.

The process whereby this system of layering is produced is termed *podsolization*, and the profile resulting is called a *podsol*. It is illustrated in Figure 2.25. This type of profile develops only (i) where precipitation exceeds evaporation and transpiration so that the overall water movement is downwards, (ii) where drainage is free, (iii) under certain vegetation types, such as coniferous forest or dwarf heath shrubs and (iv) at fairly low temperatures. The importance of vegetation is in the chemistry of the leaf fragments are common in the soil because of rock shattering by the ice, and they may be forced to the surface by freeze–thaw processes and form rings or 'polygons' (see p. 185).

Temperate grasslands have a characteristic soil associated with them, in which there is a rapid incorporation of organic litter into the soil and generally little differentiation between A and B horizons. Under hot conditions the overall movement of water through the soil may be upwards rather than downwards. Such soils are called *pedocals*, as distinct from *pedalfers* with downward water movement. This process may result in the upward movement of soluble compounds, particularly calcium carbonate, which accumulates in the upper layers. Such soils are termed *czernozems* (Fig. 2.25e). A similar process operates in many arid, desert soils and often the supply of additional water to such soils by irrigation has aggravated the problem of surface alkalinity and salinity by increasing the upward movement of salts.

In high rainfall tropical areas, pedalfer soils are formed, but the high temperatures experienced in these regions results in the mobilization of silica rather than iron and aluminium and the latter remain concentrated in the upper soil horizons. The red soils resulting are termed *lateritic* and are poor in organic matter because of the very high decay rates in tropical climates (Fig. 2.25f).

The relationship between some soil types and climate[26] is shown in Figure 2.26.

References

1   KENDEIGH S.C. (1974) *Ecology with Special Reference to Animals and Man.* Prentice Hall, New Jersey.
2   MARSHALL J.K. (1978) Factors limiting the survival of *Corynephorus canescens* (L.) Beauv. in Great Britain at the northern edge of its distribution. *Oikos* **19**, 206–216.
3   THOMPSON P.A. (1970) Germination of species of Caryophyllaceae in relation to their geographical distribution in Europe. *Ann. Bot. Lond.* **34**, 427–449.
4   WOOLHOUSE H.W. (1978) Light-gathering and carbon assimilation processes in photosynthesis; their adaptive modifications and significance for agriculture. *Endeavour N.S.* **2**, 35–46.
5   EHLERINGER J.R. (1978) Implications of quantum yield differences on the distributions of C_3 and C_4 grasses. *Oecologia (Berl.)* **31**, 255–267.
6   TEERI J.A. & STOWE L.G. (1976) Climatic patterns and the distribution of C_4 grasses in North America. *Oecologia (Berl.)* **23**, 1–12.
7   WILLIAMS G.J. & MARKLEY J.L. (1973) The photosynthetic pathway type of North American shortgrass prairie species and some ecological implications. *Photosynthetica* **7**, 262–270.
8   SPOONER G.M. (1974) The distribution of *Gammarus* species in estuaries. *J. Mar. Biol. Ass.* **27**, 1–52.
9   WARBURG M.R. (1964) The responses of isopods towards temperature, humidity and light. *Animal Behaviour* **12**, 175–186.
10 WARBURG M.R. (1968) Behavioural adaptations of terrestrial isopods. *Am. Zoologist* **8**, 545–599.
11 PARIS O.H. & SIKORA A. (1967) Radiotracer analysis of the trophic dynamics of natural isopod populations. In: Petrusewicz K. (ed.), *Secondary Productivity of Terrestrial Ecosystems*, Volume II. Warsaw.

12 LOWRY W.P. (1967) *Weather and Life: An Introduction to Biometeorology.* Academic Press, New York and London.

13 OORT A.H. The energy cycle of the earth. *Scient. Am.* **223** (3), 54–63.

14 EYRE S.R. (ed.) (1971) *World Vegetation Types.* Macmillan, London.

15 RAY P.M. & ALEXANDER W.E. (1966) Photoperiodic adaptation to latitude in *Xanthium strumasium. Am. J. Bot.* **53**, 806–816.

16 McMILLAN C. (1970) Photoperiod in *Xanthium* populations from Texas and Mexico. *Am. J. Bot.* **57**, 881–888.

17 McMILLAN C. (1973) Photoperiod evidence in the introduction of *Xanthium strumarium* to Tahiti and Hawaii from Mexico. *Am. J. Bot.* **60**, 277–282.

18 BRADSHAW W.E. (1976) Geography of photoperiodic response in diapausing mosquito. *Nature, Lond.* **262**, 284–386.

19 WALTER H. & LEITH H. (1967) *Klimadiagramm–Weltatlas.* VEB Gustav Fischer Verlag, Jena.

20 WALTER H. (1979) *Vegetation of the Earth,* 2nd edn. Springer-Verlag, New York and Heidelberg.

21 RAUNKAIER C. (1934) *The Life Forms of Plants and Statistical Plant Geography.* Clarendon Press, Oxford.

22 HARDY A. (1956) *The Open Sea.* New Naturalist Series, Collins, London.

23 LEWIS J.R. (1964) *The Ecology of Rocky Shores.* English Universities Press, London.

24 ELTRINGHAM S.K. (1971) *Life in Mud and Sand.* English Universities Press, London.

25 BRADY N.C. (1974) *The Nature and Properties of Soils,* 8th edn. Macmillan, New York.

26 WHITTAKER R.H. (1975) *Communities and Ecosystems,* 2nd edn. Macmillan, New York.

soil/decomposer part of the ecosystem than there is in the grazing food chains above the ground surface. This is true of many ecosystems.

For this particular ecosystem we know nothing of the carnivores in the system. For example, slugs, earthworms and dung invertebrates, as well as other invertebrate grazers, will be eaten by ground-feeding birds, such as the meadow pipit, or by mammals such as shrews. These in turn may be preyed upon by 'top carnivores' such as fox or kestrel. These various feeding levels are termed *trophic levels*, for example:

	Plant —	Herbivore —	Carnivore —	Top carnivore
	Grass	Crane fly larvae	Meadow pipit	Kestrel
Trophic level	1	2	3	4

One may find extra trophic levels in a food chain, for example:

Grass — Crane fly — Carnivorous — Shrew — Snake — Fox
      larvae   ground beetle

but food chains of this length are unusual. The factors which limit the number of trophic levels in an ecosystem will be considered later in this chapter.

Nutrients in the ecosystem While energy flows through the ecosystem between trophic levels, the chemical elements, of which matter is composed, cycle within the system. Some elements such as carbon and oxygen, both of which are common in gaseous compounds, move freely between ecosystems, whereas others such as phosphorus, calcium and potassium, do not have common gaseous forms and are therefore less mobile.[4] Even these, however, enter and leave ecosystems by various means. For example, precipitation brings various elements into ecosystems both in dissolved and suspended forms. In Figure 3.2, which portrays the same sheep-grazed mountain grassland ecosystem as in Figure 3.1, the amount of potassium entering the ecosystem in rainfall is as high as 0.3 g m^{-2} yr^{-1}. This high input is due to the fact that the mountains of North Wales, from which these figures were obtained, are close to the sea and the rainfall is therefore rich in a variety of elements.

Other gains to the ecosystem may result from animal migrations, the carriage of plant matter by wind or water, or by human fertilization to improve productivity. The weathering of rock materials within the soil is another source of elements for the ecosystem. The ecosystem also suffers losses, the most important of which is usually the leaching of chemicals from the plants, litter and soil as water moves through the system and out in stream flow or by soaking away to underground aquifers. It is very difficult to obtain reliable values for the rate of weathering in the soil, but it is likely to be of the same order as the leaching losses. The overall budget for an ecosystem can be given by the following equation:

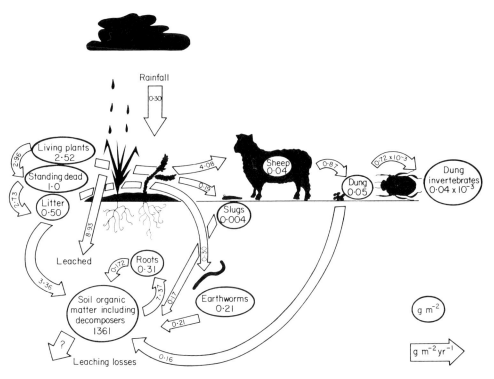

Figure 3.2. Movement and storage of potassium within a sheep-grazed upland grassland ecosystem in Wales (data from Perkins, 1978[2]). Units are g m^{-2}, or g m^{-2} yr^{-1} if figures are within arrows.

$$\text{Soil weathering} + \text{Nutrient input from rainfall, etc.} =$$
$$\text{Leaching loss} + \text{Other losses} + \text{Growth in biomass}$$

Within the ecosystem a given atom may be recycled many times before being lost. It will be moving constantly from *abiotic* (non-living) to *biotic* (living) materials and back again. Its incorporation into biotic material, as for example when it is absorbed by a plant root, involves the expenditure of energy on the part of the plant to pump it across the cell membrane. So some of the respiratory energy losses from the ecosystem are used in driving the nutrient cycles.

The distribution and flow rate of an element within an ecosystem may be of considerable interest. In the grassland system there is five times the concentration of potassium per unit area in earthworms than in sheep. Indeed, there is more potassium in sheep dung than in sheep. It is also interesting to note that the transfer of potassium to the sheep in grazing exceeds the rate of movement of potassium into the litter following death of plant tissue. This contrasts with the energy situation (Fig. 3.1).

A knowledge of the quantities and flow rates of such ecosystems helps us to manage them efficiently. If we wish to crop the ecosystem at any given trophic level (e.g. sheep at the second trophic level), then we must

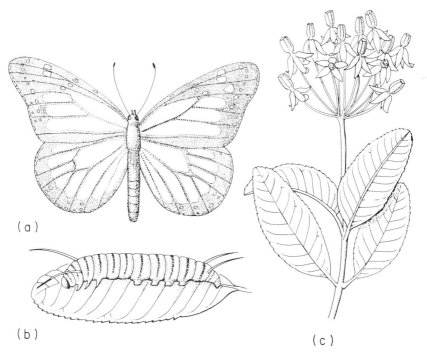

Figure 3.5. The monarch butterfly (*Danaus plexippus*): (a) adult, (b) larva and (c) its food plant, the milkweed, *Asclepias* spp. (the species illustrated is *A. amplexicaulis*).

of the olive borer move with successive generations between plant organs, seeking that which offers the richest grazing. Some grazers use several food plants; for example the plant bug, *Euryderma oleraceum*, moves among five host plant species, all of the family Cruciferae, in order to obtain maximum nitrogenous foods (i.e. those with the most protein).

When the herbivore has consumed vegetable matter, there remains the problem of digestion. The efficiency of digestion varies greatly among herbivores; generally the sap-sucking insects are more efficient than the chewers because they have less 'roughage' in their diet.

The efficiency of carnivores is normally higher than that of herbivores. They do face problems, however, such as the amount of energy they can afford to spend in the pursuit and capture of their prey. As far as digestive efficiency is concerned they are usually far more efficient than herbivores, often having values of over 70 per cent.

Overall, one can see that there can be more trophic levels present in an ecosystem if each level is efficient in both the consumption and digestion of its food. But another factor which needs to be considered is stability. If there are large and unpredictable variations in the availability of food, then the organism dependent upon it may become locally and temporarily extinct. This means that it is difficult to support a system with many trophic levels (depending upon high efficiency in resource use at any given

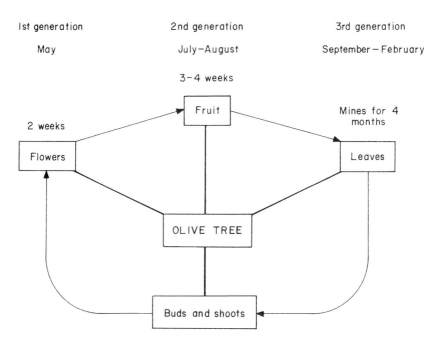

1st generation	2nd generation	3rd generation
May	July–August	September – February

3–4 weeks

Fruit

Mines for 4 months

2 weeks

Flowers

Leaves

OLIVE TREE

Buds and shoots

Figure 3.6. Movement of the olive borer (*Prays olerae*) between plant organs on the olive tree (*Olea europaea*). Each generation seeks feeding sites which offer greatest nutritional potential at that time of year.

level) if the resource itself is unreliable. For this reason, unpredictable, unstable environments have shorter food chains than stable predictable ones.[15] On the other hand, the counter argument also holds, and if we try to construct theoretical model ecosystems using computer techniques which have more than about four trophic levels they often prove unstable and collapse into shorter food chain systems.[16]

Thus, the number of trophic levels we find in natural ecosystems depends upon a complex of resource availability, resource stability and the efficiency of exploitation at each trophic level. In the sea, where food chains are long, there is high efficiency of resource use, particularly at the herbivore level, together with a high degree of predictability in the environment.

Food and distribution Many animal species have limited distributions that are associated with the distribution of the plants or other animals on which they feed. Although the caterpillars of the Chalkhill blue butterfly, *Lysandra coridon* (whose distribution was discussed in Chapter 1) may feed in the laboratory on the leaves of one or two species of plants, in the field they are found exclusively on the vetch, *Hippocrepis comosa*—and it was noted that the limited distribution of this plant is a major factor in the distribution of the butterfly. Species like this with very narrow food preferences (*stenophagous* species) are much more likely to be limited in their distribution by their food than are species with very broad food preferences (*euryphagous* species). But species with such catholic tastes as the American bobwhite quail (*Colinus virginianus*) which was found to feed on the fruits and seeds of 927 different plant species (as well as on many insects and spiders) are unlikely to have distributions limited by food preferences. In general, herbivorous species have more restricted food requirements, and therefore distributions more limited by food, than do carnivores. One reason for this might be that in most habitats there is a much smaller quantity of animal food available to the carnivorous species than plant food for herbivores, and if carnivores had very limited food preferences they might often have to go for long periods without food. But even among herbivorous species there is great variation in the degree of restriction to particular food. For instance, in a survey of the feeding habits of 240 species of aphids or 'plant-lice' which suck plant juices, it was found that 27 per cent of them were restricted to a single species of plant, 40 per cent to a group of closely related species, and 33 per cent fed on many different species. Amongst herbivores as a whole, the most common types are probably those that feed on a group of closely related species.

A good example of a herbivore of this type is the Colorado potato beetle, *Leptinotarsa decemlineata*, which is found naturally in the eastern Rocky Mountain region where it feeds mostly on the wild sand-bur (*Solanum rostratum*). When a closely related species, the domesticated potato (*S. tuberosum*) was widely introduced from its original home in the Andes, the Colorado beetle was able to use this new food supply, and has thereby been able to extend its distribution right across North America and even to many parts of Europe (Fig. 3.7).

There is, however, an exception to the rule that carnivores tend to be

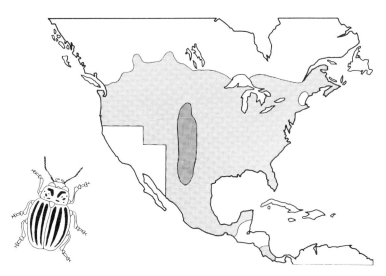

Figure 3.7. Distribution of the Colorado beetle in North and Central America. Original distribution in dark shading; 1962 distribution in light shading.

less limited by food than herbivores; this is to be found in those animal species that are parasites of others. Most of these can obtain their food and the living conditions that they require from only one, or at best very few, species of host. Their distributions, therefore, are strongly limited by that of their hosts.

One also finds that some food plant species support more herbivores than others. T. R. E. Southwood analysed data concerning the association of insect species with British trees[17] and he found that there was a strong correlation between the number of subfossil occurrences of tree species in Britain during the last 10 000 years and the number of insects associated with them (Fig. 3.8). The number of subfossil occurrences is itself

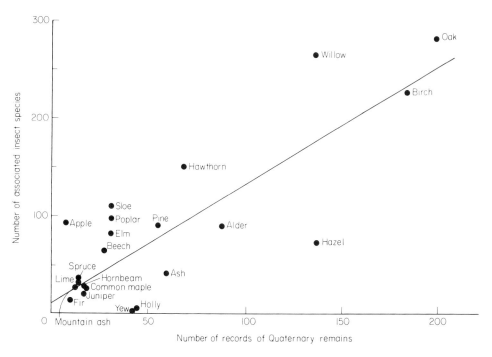

Figure 3.8. Number of insect species associated with various trees in Britain as a function of the number of subfossil records from Quaternary deposits (about the last two million years). (After Southwood, 1961.[17])

dependent upon two factors, the range of a species and its abundance within Britain through the time in question and the period of time during which it has been present. The older and more widespread and abundant a tree species was in the past, the more species of insect are currently associated with it. H. J. B. Birks has questioned the use of subfossil abundance as an indicator of true abundance on the grounds that some species produce more and better dispersed remains than others, and will thus be over-represented in the fossil record.[18] He has shown that the number of insect species associated with British trees is positively correlated with the time for which it has been present in these islands (Fig. 3.9).

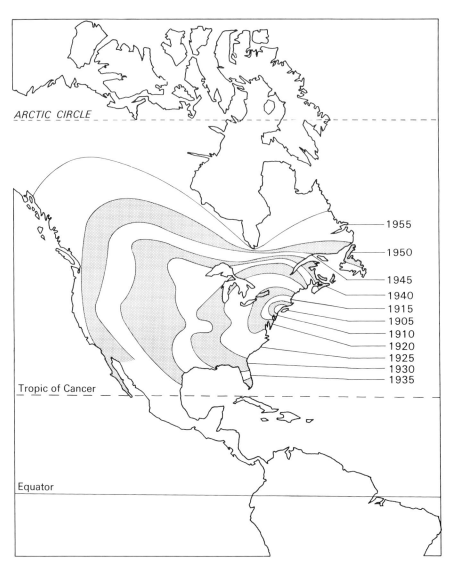

ARCTIC CIRCLE

1955
1950
1945
1940
1915
1905
1910
1920
1925
1930
1935

Tropic of Cancer

Equator

Figure 3.10. Gradual extension of the distribution of the European starling in North America from 1905 to 1955.

coniferous woodland, however, the red squirrel is apparently still the more successful, and the grey squirrel has rarely succeeded in occupying these areas. Where the grey squirrel has replaced the native red, it probably has done so by virtue of its superior adaptability to the niche of herbivore at canopy level in deciduous woodland.

There is good evidence that, in the past, whole faunas have invaded new areas and eliminated the native species by successful competition. For example, North and South America were separated by sea until the end of the Pliocene Period (about two million years ago). The Isthmus of Panama

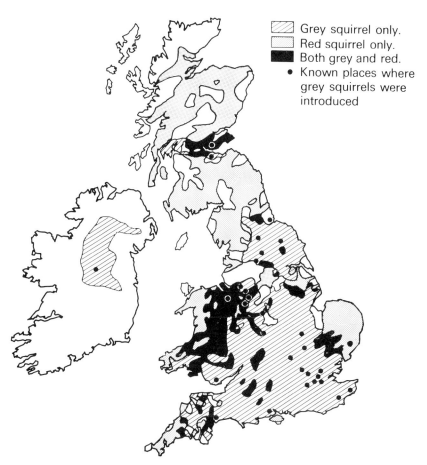

Grey squirrel only.
Red squirrel only.
Both grey and red.
• Known places where grey squirrels were introduced

Figure 3.11. Map of squirrel distribution in Britain. (After *Sunday Times* Publications.)

then came into being and enabled South American species to invade northwards and North American species southwards. In general, the northern species proved to be the more successful in competition and most of the characteristic South American fauna of this time became extinct; but very few North American species were wiped out by the South American invaders—probably because the North American herbivores were more efficient and the predators more successful.[21]

Despite these dramatic examples of invasion and competitive displacement, it is most likely that, in natural situations, species that compete for food or other resources have evolved means of reducing the pressures of competition and of dividing up the resources between them. This is mutually advantageous since it reduces the risk of either species being eliminated and made extinct by competition with the others. This is an advantage not only to the species directly involved but to the whole community of species in the habitat, since it results in *more* species, depending on as many different sources of food as possible. In such communities competition occurs between so many different species, each with its own specialized adaptations, that no single species can become so numerous as to displace others. This results in a greater degree of stability for the community, and stable communities are strongly resistant to the invasion of new species which might disrupt the highly evolved pattern of competition within them.

Case history of an ecosystem   It is rare to be able to document precisely the effects of the introduction of a radically new element into an established ecosystem. This is because such studies have usually commenced only after the effects had become obvious, and there was therefore no information on the structure of the original ecosystem. An exception to this has been the introduction of the cichlid fish *Cichla ocellaris* into Lake Gatun, in the Panama Canal Zone.[22] This region has already been extensively studied, and it is also still possible to study the original ecosystem in parts of the lake that *Cichla* has not, as yet, reached (Fig. 3.12). The original ecosystem contained 14 species of fish, 11 of which contributed significantly to the total biomass. In the *Cichla*-dominated regions, 7 of these 11 species have disappeared completely, and three others have been severely reduced. Only one, *Cichlasoma*, has increased, probably because *Cichla* has eliminated those species which formerly preyed on it.

The changes in the ecosystem have also included the structure of the zooplankton community, and the fish-eating bird community of the lake. More significantly for man himself, the reduction in fish diversity seems to have been the cause of an increase in the numbers of mosquitoes in the region, presumably because the now absent species of fish were controlling the population of aquatic mosquito larvae. Several serious outbreaks of malaria (a disease transmitted by mosquitoes) have taken place close to the *Cichla*-dominated parts of the lake—a result that would at first sight seem to have little connection with the introduction of a single new species of fish into the lake.

Reducing competition   Many different ways of reducing competition between species have evolved. Sometimes species with similar food or space requirements exploit the same resources at different seasons of the year, or even at different times of day. A common system amongst predatory mammals and birds is for one species (or a group of them) to have evolved specialized night-time activity whilst another species or group of species are day-time predators in the same habitats. An example amongst birds is the owls on the one hand, many species of which hunt at night, judging distance mostly by ear, and the hawks and falcons on the other, which are day-time hunters, with extremely keen eyesight, especially adapted for judging distances accurately. Thus, both groups of predators can co-exist in the same stretch of country, and prey on the same

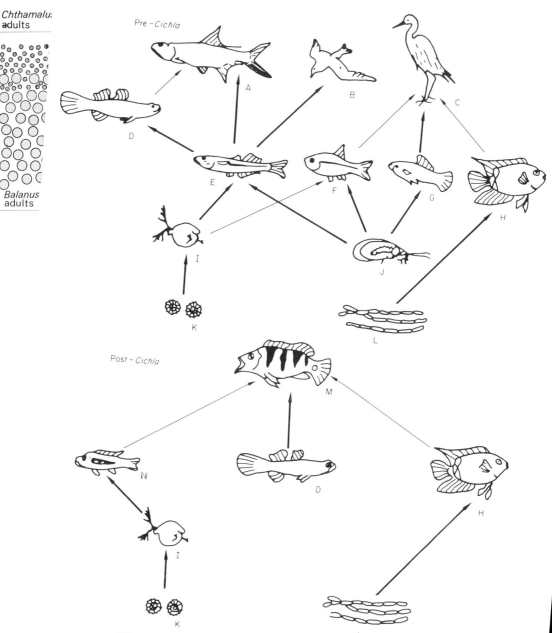

Figure 3.12. Generalized food webs of common Gatun Lake populations. Thick arrows indicate that food item is of major importance to predator or herbivore; thin arrows indicate minor importance. Key to species: (A) *Tarpon atlanticus*; (B) *Chlidonias niger*; (C) several species of herons and kingfishers; (D) *Gobiomorus dormitor*; (E) *Melaniris chagresi*; (F) Characinidae; (G) Poeciliidae, including two common species; (H) *Cichlasoma maculicauda*; (I) zooplankton; (J) terrestrial insects; (K) small phytoplankton; (L) filamentous green algae; (M) adult *Cichla ocellaris*; (N) young *Cichla*. (After A. Spight. From Zaret and Paine, 1973.[22])

appearance of its leaves and flowers. The British ecologist Sir Arthur Tansley performed experiments on the two species.[26] He found that in a greenhouse both species would grow in either acid or alkaline soils, although each species grew best on the type of soil in which it was most commonly found. He then grew a mixture of the two species on the two types of soil. He found the G. pumilum grew so much faster on alkaline soils that it crowded out G. saxatile, by filling the space available for roots and shading it from sunlight. Similarly, G. saxatile was the more successful competitor on acid soils. Tansley suggested that the distribution of the two species could be largely explained by these competition effects, and by differences in their relative growth rates in the two types of soil. G. saxatile is absent even on some acid soils, perhaps because conditions are such that other vigorously growing acid soil species have there been able to take its place.

Changing chaffinches   Sometimes closely related species that have evolved in different geographical regions extend their geographical ranges till their distributions overlap. When such species have similar requirements for food and space, the pressure of competition may cause one or both species to change its habits. One such species is the chaffinch, *Fringilla coelebs*, which is found all over Europe and north-east Africa. It has very wide ecological tolerance and is one of the two or three most common birds over much of its range. It nests in a wide variety of habitats, including both coniferous and deciduous forest, as well as in parks and gardens. At some time in its history the chaffinch has invaded the Canary Islands, which lie one to two hundred miles off the north-west African coast. On two of the bigger islands, Grand Canary and Tenerife, the colonizing chaffinches have evolved into a new species, the blue chaffinch, *F. teydea*. At some more recent time a second wave of colonists belonging to the parent species, *F. coelebs*, has reached the islands and, although they have not evolved into a new species, they have become a sub-species, *F. coelebs canariensis*. This form is forced to compete for food and nesting sites with the blue chaffinch.[27] In contrast to its ubiquitous distribution elsewhere, *F. coelebs* is found in these islands to breed only in the deciduous forests (which are mostly of sweet chestnuts and laurel), while the blue chaffinch occupies the coniferous forest. Clearly, the presence of the blue chaffinch restricts *F. coelebs* to those habitats in which it is the more effective competitor. This is confirmed by the fact that in the most westerly island, Palma, from which the blue chaffinch is for some reason absent, *F. coelebs* occupies the same range of forest habitats as in Europe.

Predators and prey   Predators may be another biological factor influencing the distribution of species, but their effects have been much less studied than those of competition. The simplest influences that predators might have is to eliminate species by eating them, or alternatively, to prevent the entry of new ones into a habitat. There is very little evidence that either of these processes are common in nature. One or two experimental studies have shown that predators sometimes eat all the representatives of a species in their environment, particularly when the species is already rare. But all such studies have been made in rather artificial situations in which a predator is introduced into a community of species that have reached some sort of balance with their environment in the absence of any predator; such communities are not at all like natural communities which already include predators. In general, it is not in the interests of predatory species to eliminate a prey species, because if they do this they destroy a potential source of food. Probably most natural communities have evolved so that there is a great number of potential prey species available to each predatory species. Thus no species is preyed upon too heavily, and the predators can always turn to alternative food species if the numbers of their usual prey should be reduced by climatic or other influences.

As mentioned earlier, competition may prevent two species from living together in a habitat, and may modify the distribution of species, because the resources of the habitat are inadequate to support both of them. Probably the most important effect of predators and of parasites and disease (which are 'internal' predators) on the distribution of species is that, by feeding on the individuals of more than one species, they reduce the pressures of competition between them. Thus, by reducing pressures on the resources of the habitat, predators may allow more species to survive than would survive if the predators were not there. Nearly 20 years ago it was shown by laboratory experiments that if two species of seed-eating beetle (weevils) were kept together in jars of wheat, one species always eliminated the other within five generations. One of the two species always multiplied faster than the other, and this species won in the competition for food and places to lay eggs. But if a predator was introduced, such as a parasitic wasp, whose larvae feed inside the bodies of the beetle larvae of either species and eventually kill them, both species persisted. The numbers of both species were kept so low by the predator that competition for food, which would have caused one or other to be eliminated, never occurred.

More recent studies of natural communities have largely confirmed the hypothesis that predators may actually *increase* the number of different species that can live in a habitat. The American ecologist, Robert T. Paine, made an especially fine study on the animal community of a rocky shore on the Pacific coast of North America.[28] The community included 15 species, comprising acorn barnacles, limpets, chitons, mussels, dog whelks and one major predator, the starfish, *Pisaster ochraceus*, which fed on all the other species. Paine carried out an experiment on a small area of the shore in which he removed all the starfish and prevented any others from entering. Within a few months 60–80 per cent of the available space in the experimental area was occupied by newly-settled barnacles, which began to grow over other species and to eliminate them. After a year or so, however, the barnacles themselves began to be crowded out by large numbers of small, but rapidly growing mussels, and when the study ended these completely dominated the community, which now consisted of only eight species. The removal of predators thus resulted in the halving of the number of species and there was evidence, too, that the number of plant species of the community (rock-encrusting algae) was also reduced, because of the competition with barnacles and mussels for the available space.

A general conclusion then is that the presence of predators in a well-balanced community is likely to increase rather than reduce the numbers of species present, so that, overall, predators broaden the distribution of species. Only a few experiments similar to Paine's have been performed and so one must be cautious about applying this conclusion to all communities. There is some independent evidence, however, that herbivores, which act on plants as predators do on their prey, may similarly increase the number of plant species that can live in a habitat. In the last century, Charles Darwin noticed that in southern England, meadowland grazed by sheep often contained as many as 20 species of plants, while neglected, ungrazed land contained only about 11 species. He suggested that fast-growing, tall grasses were controlled by sheep grazing in the meadow, but that in ungrazed land these species grew tall so that they shaded the small slow-growing plants from the sun and eliminated them. A similar process occurred in chalk grassland areas in Britain, when the disease myxomatosis caused the death of large numbers of rabbits; the resulting reduction in grazing allowed considerable invasion by coarse grasses and scrub. As a result many of these areas are much less rich in species than they were under heavy 'predation'.

On the Washington coast Paine performed another series of experiments in which he removed the sea-urchin *Strongylocentrotus purpuratus*, which grazes on algae.[29] Initially, there was an increase in the number of species of algae present: the six or so new species were probably ones that were normally grazed too heavily by the sea-urchin to survive in the habitat. But over two or three years the picture changed as the community of algae gradually became dominated by two species, *Hedophyllum sessile* on exposed parts of the shore, and *Laminaria groenlandica* in the more sheltered regions below low-water mark. These two species were tall and probably 'shaded out' the smaller species, as did the tall grasses studied by Darwin. The total number of species present was in the end greatly reduced after the removal of the herbivores.

The activities of carnivorous predators in a community also have an effect on the plants since, by limiting to some extent the number of their herbivorous prey, they prevent over-grazing, and thus reduce the risk of rare species of plants being eliminated.

The niche   It seems, then, that competition for food or space, sometimes influenced by predators or grazing, is the main biological factor influencing the distribution of animal and plant species. The range of physical factors of the environment to which a species is adapted largely determines its range on a geographical or habitat scale, but within this range the survival of the species depends on its ability to compete for resources with other species living there. To understand the full significance of this for biogeography, some basic points of ecological theory must be considered. The first of these is the concept of the *ecological niche*. The ecological niche of a species (sometimes referred to simply as the 'niche') is the way of life or 'profession' that it practises in the particular part of the environment in which it lives. For instance, the niche of *Pisaster ochraceus*, the starfish studied by Paine, is that of the main predator of the rocky shores of the Pacific coast of North America. Similarly, the niche of the grey squirrel *Sciurus carolinensis*, is that of nut, seed and catkin feeder of the canopy level of mainly deciduous woodland of the eastern United States (and now also of the southern British Isles). The niche of a species is defined, then, in terms of both its food and its habitat or microhabitat. It can be stated as a general principle that no two species can have the same ecological niche. When species compete for a niche, one will almost always be eliminated. This is the *principle of competitive exclusion*, referred to earlier in the chapter, and originally suggested by the Russian biologist G. F. Gause[30] in the 1930s. Though it has since been realized that there are one or two 'modifying clauses' which must be added to this principle, later work has shown it to be largely valid. Many cases have been observed where two or more species in a community seem at first sight to be occupying the same niche, but more detailed work has shown that they differ somewhat in their food habits, or in the area of the habitat in which they live. In some cases species may share part of their range of food or space with others, but usually each species has part of its niche, some food materials or a specialized microhabitat which is exclusively its own, and this acts as a refuge from competition with other species. No case of two species having the same niche has been demonstrated. A possible exception might arise in cases where the number of competing species is kept so low by a common predator that they never reach levels at which they might compete. This situation may be common, but no example has been studied in detail.

There have been some fine studies of the ways in which groups of closely related species with similar food or space requirements have evolved in such a way that a division of their resources into a series of distinct ecological niches has resulted, so that they do not compete with each other. One of the best of these was carried out by Robert H. MacArthur of Princeton University, who contributed much to our understanding of the ecological niche.[31] In north-eastern North America, five species of warbler often live together in coniferous forest. All belong to the same genus, *Dendroica*, and are very closely related; they all feed on insects and have similar requirements for nest sites. MacArthur found that the species showed complex differences in feeding and nesting behaviour which gave each one a distinct niche, and prevented competition, at least at times when food was plentiful. This is shown in Figure 3.14.

There are certain difficulties in applying the concept of the ecological niche to plants. Nearly all plants need sunlight for photosynthesis and, at least in terrestrial environments, they tend to occupy the same part of the habitat—the region just above and below the soil surface. Indeed to a great

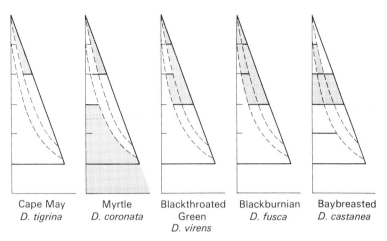

Cape May	Myrtle	Blackthroated	Blackburnian	Baybreasted
D. tigrina	D. coronata	Green	D. fusca	D. castanea
		D. virens		

Figure 3.14. Feeding zones on spruce trees of five species of North American warbler, *Dendroica*. The tree is shown diagrammatically, having been divided into six zones each 10 feet high, also into an outer zone of new needles and buds, a middle zone of old needles, and an inner zone of bare or lichen-covered branches. The shaded areas indicate regions where the species concerned spends at least half of its feeding time.

extent the plants actually form the microhabitats amongst which the animals of the community are distributed. Nevertheless, plant species do show differences in the areas they occupy horizontally and vertically in the habitat, and also in their seasons of growth and flowering. These differences are comparable to the ecological niches of animals, and there is little doubt that the principle of competitive exclusion applies equally well to plants and to animals.

What are the factors that determine which species will occupy a niche when two or more species are competing for it? Experiments have shown that the species that wins the competition in a particular environment is the one best adapted to the range of physical conditions present. The winner is the species that can maintain the faster rate of population growth—the highest birth rate and the lowest death rate—under the particular conditions of the environment. In other words, it is the species that can use the food resources and living-space most efficiently.

This is a most important conclusion for the biogeographer since it makes clear the difficulties that species have in broadening or changing their distributions. Simplifying somewhat, there are four possible results if a species is entering a geographical region or habitat which it has not previously inhabited.

First, the individuals of the species that are invading may be eliminated because they are not sufficiently well adapted to the physical conditions of the region or habitat to compete successfully with species occupying suitable ecological niches. This is probably the case with the 50 or 60 species of birds that are 'accidental' visitors to the British Isles. Many will leave as they have come, others will die of starvation and some may fall

Making a Living

prey to predators. The end result is the same: that the species fails to establish itself permanently.

Second, the species may prove to be such a successful competitor that it is the native species, at present occupying the niche, that is eliminated. This is what has occurred with the North American grasses mentioned earlier. The invader, *Bromus tectorum*, has eliminated *Agropyron spicatum* and other native species from parts of the United States.

Third, the invading species may prove to be an efficient competitor in parts of the niche of a native species and may succeed in displacing it from this part of the niche, which then becomes two smaller niches. Probably this is what has occurred in the case of the two species of chaffinch (discussed on p. 86) in the Canary Islands. *Fringilla coelebs* has succeeded in displacing the blue chaffinch, *F. teydea*, from part of its niche in the islands where both species occur, and the original niche now consists of two niches, a coniferous one, occupied by *F. teydea*, and a deciduous one occupied by *F. coelebs*. A similar situation exists with the two species of squirrel in the British Isles.

Fourth, there are some circumstances in which an invading species is fortunate enough to find its normal niche vacant. This often happens because the whole ecosystem is in an early stage of development and sufficient time has not passed for the species in question to have invaded. In such an instance there is little or no competitive resistance to the invasion of the new species.

Ecological succession   The idea that the ecosystem, or the plant community, passes through a series of developmental stages before finally achieving a balanced or equilibrium state, was first proposed by the American ecologist F. E. Clements,[32] and has since been expanded and developed by a number of biologists. When ecosystems begin their development, following the destruction of a prior ecosystem by a catastrophe such as fire, or as a result of the emergence of a new area suitable for colonization, as was the case when the volcanic island of Surtsey was thrown up from the sea off Iceland or when a shingle bar or sandbank comes into existence, the physical factors of the environment are usually most severe and very few species are capable of survival. The very presence of a growing plant, however, modifies the physical environment in such a way that the invasion of further species is facilitated. In particular, one finds higher organic matter contents in the soil, reduced windspeed and therefore higher relative humidity at the soil surface, less severe temperature fluctuations both diurnally and seasonally in the layers near the soil, and many other microclimatic modifications.

In their growth the plants make available many new food sources and microhabitats for herbivores, and the establishment of these in turn creates new niches for predators. The invasion of new plant species brings new opportunities for further animals. Short-lived, opportunist species which succeed well in the open, unstable conditions of the early stages of succession are gradually replaced by longer-lived species which are often more specialized in their habitat requirements. In the early stages the plant community is usually poor in species and one often finds that a few species dominate the scene. As time passes, not only does the community become richer in species, but there is also a tendency for the available space to be more equably divided between the species present. This effect can be seen in the data shown in Figure 3.15, which are derived from a

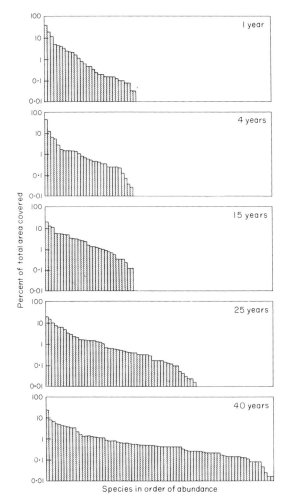

Figure 3.15. Increasing species diversity in an old field succession in Illinois. Species are ranked in order of abundance, the latter being expressed as percentage area covered on a log scale. Data from Bazzaz (after May, 1978[34]).

succession developed on abandoned agricultural fields in Illinois which have been studied by F. A. Bazzaz.[33]

Eventually the *climax community* evolves and the creation of new ecological niches ceases. If a new species is to invade a climax community, it must displace an existing species from its niche without the help of changes in the environment unfavourable to the current occupant. This is why climax communities are much more stable and less open to invasion than the earlier stages of succession.

Even in climax communities, it is sometimes possible to recognize ecological niches that are vacant and would be available to an invader.[34] For instance, the tropical rain forest of the East Indies contains about 27 species of woodpeckers, which feed mostly on the insects in living or dead tree trunks and branches. The forest of New Guinea, only a few hundred miles to the east, contains not a single woodpecker. No native species have evolved to fill this niche, and apparently none of the East Indies species have invaded, so that the niche remains without an occupant. About 12 species of fish from the Red Sea have become established in the eastern Mediterranean after invading through the Suez Canal. They seem to have found unoccupied niches in the Mediterranean, because several have become quite abundant (some have become important to the fishing industry) and yet no native species appears to have suffered.

Gradients of diversity   Many different types of organism show a pronounced gradient of diversity, the number of species or genera increasing as one moves from high latitudes towards the tropics. For example, Figure 3.16 shows how the number of species of birds breeding in various regions of North and Central America increases from the north to the tropical regions. Panama, only 500 miles north of the Equator, has about three times as many species as Alaska, which is many times its area.

One of the reasons for this increasing diversity becomes apparent if the

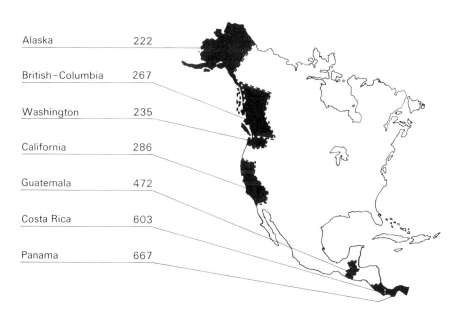

Figure 3.16. Number of bird species in different parts of North and Central America.

ways of life of the species are analysed. For example, if the mammal fauna of forest areas in the tundra of Fairbanks, Alaska (65°N), the deciduous forest of southern Michigan (42°N), and the moist tropical forest of Panama (9°N) are compared, some interesting facts emerge.[35] Firstly, much of the increased species diversity is due to an increase in the diversity of bats, which is responsible for nearly one-third of the increase between Alaska and Michigan, and for over two-thirds of that between Michigan and Panama (Fig. 3.17). Secondly, much of the tropical diversity is here due to the appearance of a purely fruit-eating way of life, and to a great increase in the number of insectivores, many preying on insects which are themselves feeding on the fruit. The evolution of fruit and of fruit-eating animals has clearly proceeded hand in hand. The fruit provides food for the animals, which in turn provide a dispersal mechanism that is vital in

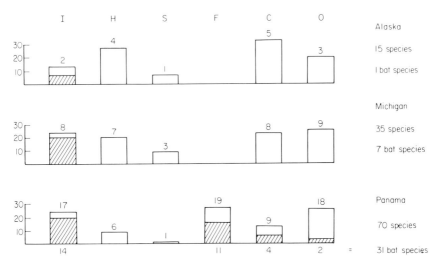

Figure 3.17. The diversity of mammals in forest areas at three different latitudes. The heights of the columns indicate the percentage of the total mammal species that are insectivorous (I), herbivorous (H), seed-eating (S), fruit-eating (F), carnivorous (C) or omnivorous (O). The number above each column shows the total number of species with that diet. The shaded parts indicate the proportion of bat species, and the numbers below the Panama columns show the number of bat species with that diet. (Data from Fleming, 1973.[35])

the almost windless forest—they may carry fruit for considerable distances before the seeds are scattered when the fruit is eaten, or contained in the animals' droppings.

The appearance of the purely fruit-eating niche is partly due to the fact that the tropics are a region of greater climatic stability. There are no marked seasons of higher or lower temperature and, even though there are seasons of higher or lower rainfall, there is always enough rainfall for some trees to be fruiting. For example, the manakin *Manacus* consumes up to 38 different species of fruit per month during the wet season, but still finds six different species of fruit during the driest month.

Though some fruit and seeds fall to the ground, there is clearly an advantage in being able to reach them while they are still attached to the tree. Flying animals are also able to catch the rich insect life on the wing, and to move from tree to tree with the greatest safety and economy of effort. It is therefore not surprising to find an increased number of climbing and flying animals in the tropics, notably birds and bats.

But climatic stability is not the only factor permitting animals in the tropical forest to rely wholly upon a diet of fruit. Another factor is the extreme diversity of trees in this region, which ensures that a failure in the fruit crop from one species of tree will not have serious effects on the population sizes of the fruit-eating animals. The diversity of trees is shown by the fact that there may be as many as 300 species of tree in 2 km² of Brazilian rain forest (though the majority of these are represented by only a few specimens). As one might expect, then, the fundamental reason for the diversity of animal life in the tropics is the diversity of plant life—especially, in the rain forest, the diversity of trees. How may this diversity, in turn, be explained? This question has proved to be difficult to answer and is still the subject of debate.[36]

One suggestion is that it has been possible for the tropical ecosystem to attain greater complexity because it has been almost unaffected by the ecologically immense changes that the Ice Ages caused in higher latitudes. On this hypothesis, the tropics alone are ecologically mature; the other regions have a potential species diversity much higher than that shown at present, and which will only appear in the distant future—provided that no further Ice Ages occur. The rate of recolonization of the temperate regions from the tropics has been reduced, and the disparity between the ecological diversity of the two regions has been exaggerated, by an unfortunate geographical coincidence. Almost everywhere in the world, the two regions are separated by a major geographical barrier: the Panama Isthmus, the Mediterranean, the deserts of North Africa and the Middle East, and the Himalayan Mountains. However, the gradient of diversity can also be seen within the higher latitudes, from the temperate regions towards the poles. The effects of the Ice Ages and the geography of the world may, therefore, explain the precise shape of the gradient of diversity today, but they do not explain its existence. Furthermore, it is now clear that even the tropical regions were affected by the Ice Ages, when much of these areas were arid (see p. 194).

Nevertheless, it does seem likely that there is also a greater inherent potential diversity in the tropics, and that this is related to the greater input of solar energy there, which should cause a greater amount of plant productivity in those regions. However, though the greater amount of available energy might allow a more rapid growth of the individual plant and thus explain the great height of the rain forest trees, it is not clear how this effect could become translated into greater species diversity. It has been suggested that the higher plant productivity has the effect of increasing the amount of biological competition in the tropics, whereas evolution in higher latitudes is conditioned largely by physical factors. Increased competition in the tropics might force organisms into narrower ecological niches (a possibility also aided by the lack of seasonality, so that the niche is continuously available throughout the year), and thus allow the habitat to be subdivided into a greater number of niches. However, there is no clear evidence that the great number of different species of tree in the Brazilian rain forest are each adapted to even a subtly different role in the biome.

In any case, it is not even true that all productive regions are richer in species than less productive environments. Estuaries and papyrus swamps, for example, are regions of very high productivity but, though the population of each species is very high, the number of species in each is quite low. On the other hand, such environments as deserts or the deep ocean floor have a very low productivity but are extremely rich in species, though the density of each species is low. The gradient of diversity in the sea therefore runs in the opposite direction to that on land, for it is highest in the region of low productivity (the deep sea floor) and lowest in the region of highest productivity (the estuary).

It was the American ecologist Howard Sanders who realized that the common factor underlying these two gradients is that diversity is lowest in regions of great stress.[37] Just as the more northern regions on land suffer from extremes of cold and of seasonal change, so the estuary is a region where the salinity is constantly changing due to tidal action and due to storms or floods. At the other extreme, both the tropical rain forest and the deep sea floor are stable regions, in which the environment changes very little. Sanders therefore suggested that the key to the problem lay in the rate of extinction. New species are gradually appearing both in the stable environments and in the varying, stressful environments, but the rate at which they become extinct will differ, being much higher in the varying environments than in the stable environments. This difference will allow more species to accumulate in the stable environment. This hypothesis also explains the low diversity of species in ecosystems which do not persist for long. For example, a papyrus swamp is merely a passing phase in the ecological succession, so that it has only a short span of existence in which to accumulate species. Sanders' hypothesis, known as the stability–time hypothesis, now seems the most convincing explanation of the existence of gradients of species diversity.

Equivalent species   The same niche may often be occupied by different species in different areas of a single biome. In the grassland biome there is a niche for a fairly large herbivore, usually living in herds, and often adapted for fast running. In North America the niche is (or rather was) occupied by the bison in some regions and the pronghorn antelope in others, in Africa by many species of antelope, gazelles, the zebra and eland, in Eurasia by wild horses and asses, in South America by the pampas deer (*Odocioleus bezoarticus*) and the guanaco (*Lama huanacus*) and in Australia by kangaroos and wallabies. Such groups of species, occupying the same niche in different biomes, are called *ecologically equivalent species*. As these examples show, equivalent species are not necessarily closely related, and quite different types of animals and plants may occupy the same niche in different places (such as the kangaroos in Australia and the ecologically equivalent pampas deer of South America). This is because species tend to evolve to fill particular niches as a result of the pressures of competition, and sometimes of predation, in the community in which they live. Which species evolves to fill a particular niche is largely the result of historical and geographical accident. The development of adaptations enabling a species to occupy a particular niche enables it to escape from the pressure of competition that affects it elsewhere and results in the formation of a new species. This process of the evolution of species to fill niches that are available is called *adaptive radiation*. The way this occurs and the role of evolution in the distribution of species is the subject of the next chapter.

References

1   ODUM E.P. (1959) *Fundamentals of Ecology*, 2nd edn. W.B. Saunders, Philadelphia and London.
2   PERKINS D.F. (1978) The distribution and transfer of energy and nutrients in the *Agrostis–Festuca* grassland ecosystem. In: Heal O.W. and Perkins D.F. (eds), *Production Ecology of British Moors and Montane Grasslands*, pp. 375–395. Springer-Verlag, Berlin, Heidelberg and New York.
3   LIETH H. (1973) Primary production: terrestrial ecosystems. *Human Ecol.* 1, 303–332.
4   BORMANN F.H. & LIKENS G.E. (1975) Nutrient cycling. *Science, N.Y.* 155, 424–429.
5   LIETH H. & WHITTAKER R.H. (1975) *Primary Productivity of the Biosphere.* Springer-Verlag, Berlin, Heidelberg and New York.
6   JORDAN C.F. (1971) A world pattern in plant energetics. *Am. Scient.* 59, 425–433.
7   LINDEMAN R.L. (1942) The trophic dynamic aspect of ecology. *Ecology* 23, 399–418.
8   ODUM H.T. (1957) Trophic structure and productivity of Silver Springs, Florida. *Ecol. Monogr.* 27, 55–112.
9   JUDAY C. (1942) The summer standing crop of plants and animals in four Wisconsin lakes. *Trans. Wisconsin Acad. Sci.* 34, 103–135.
10 RICKLEFS R.E. (1979) *Ecology*, 2nd edn. Chiron Press, London.
11 TAYLOR R.D. & WALKER B.H. (1978) Comparisons of vegetation use and herbivore biomass on a Rhodesian game and cattle ranch. *J. appl. Ecol.* 15, 565–581.
12 WHITTAKER R.H. & FEENEY P.P. (1971) Allelochemics: chemical interactions between species. *Science* 171, 757–770.
13 FREELAND W.J. & JANZEN D.H. (1974) Strategies in herbivory by mammals; the role of plant secondary compounds. *Am. Nat.* 108, 269–289.
14 McNEILL S. & SOUTHWOOD T.R.E. (1978) The role of nitrogen in the development of insect/plant relationships. In: Harbourne J.B. and van Emden H.F. (eds), *Biochemical Aspects of Insect/Plant Interactions*, pp. 77–98. Academic Press, New York and London.
15 MAY R.M. (1975) *Stability and Complexity in Model Ecosystems.* Princeton University Press, Princeton.
16 MAY R.M. (1976) *Theoretical Ecology: Principles and Applications.* Blackwell Scientific Publications, Oxford.
17 SOUTHWOOD T.R.E. (1961) The number of species of insect associated with various trees. *J. Anim. Ecol.* 30, 1–8.
18 BIRKS H.J.B. (1979) British trees and insects: a test of the geological-time hypothesis over the last 13 000 years. *Am. Nat.* In press.

19 HANSON H.C. & CHURCHILL E.D. (1961) *The Plant Community.* Chapman and Hall, London; Reinhold, New York.

20 SHORTEN M. (1954) *Squirrels.* Collins, London.

21 WEBB S.D. (1978) A history of savannah vertebrates in the New World. Part II: South America and the Great Interchange. *Ann. Rev. Ecol. Syst.* **9**, 393–426.

22 ZARET T.M. & PAINE R.T. (1973) Species introduction in a tropical lake. *Science* **182**, 445–449.

23 BELL R.H.V. (1970) The use of the herb layer by grazing ungulates in the Serengeti. In: Watson A. (ed.), *Animal Populations in Relation to their Food Resources*, pp. 111–127. Blackwell Scientific Publications, Oxford.

24 ODUM E.P. (1975) *Ecology*, 2nd edn. Holt, Rinehart and Winston, London and New York.

25 CONNELL J. (1961) The influence of interspecific competition and other factors on the distribution of the barnacle *Chthamalus stellatus. Ecology* **42**, 710–723.

26 TANSLEY A.G. (1917) On competition between *Galium saxatile* and *Galium sylvestre* on different types of soil. *J. Ecol.* **5**, 173–179.

27 LACK D. & SOUTHERN H.N. (1949) Birds on Tenerife. *Ibis* **91**, 607–626.

28 PAINE R.T. (1966) Food web complexity and species diversity. *Am. Natur.* **100**, 65–75.

29 PAINE R.T. & VADAS R.L. (1969) The effect of grazing in the sea urchin *Strongylocentrotus* on benthic algal populations. *Limnol. Oceanogr.* **14**, 710–719.

30 GAUSE G.F. (1934) *The Struggle for Existence.* Williams and Wilkins, Baltimore.

31 MACARTHUR R.H. (1958) Population ecology of some warblers of north-eastern coniferous forests. *Ecology* **39**, 599–619.

32 CLEMENTS F.E. (1936) Nature and structure of the climax: *J. Ecol.* **24**, 252–284.

33 BAZZAZ F.A. (1975) Plant species diversity in old field successional ecosystems in southern Illinois. *Ecology* **56**, 485–488.

34 MAY R.M. (1978) The evolution of ecological systems. *Scient. Am.* **239** (3), 118–133.

35 FLEMING T.H. (1973) Numbers of mammal species in North and Central American forest communities. *Ecology* **54**, 555–563.

36 PIANKA E.R. (1966) Latitudinal gradients in species diversity; a review of concepts. *Am. Nat.* **100**, 33–46.

37 SLOBODKIN L.B. & SANDERS H.L. (1969) On the contribution of environmental predictability to species diversity. In *Diversity and Stability in Ecological Systems*. Brookhaven Symposium in Biology, **22**, 82–95.

CHAPTER 4
THE SOURCE OF NOVELTY

Some insects are protected from detection by predators by having an almost perfect resemblance to a leaf or a twig. This is perhaps the most dramatic example of the intricate way in which an organism is adapted to its environment. Other adaptations are just as intricate and thorough, although not so obvious. Every aspect of the environment makes its demand upon the structure or the physiology of the organism: the average state of the physical conditions, together with their daily and annual ranges of variation; the changing patterns of supply and abundance of food; the occasional increased losses due to disease, to predators, or to the increased competition from other organisms at the same level in the ecological food web. Every species of animal or plant must be adapted to all these conditions; it must be able to tolerate and survive the hostile aspects of its environment, and yet able to take advantage of its opportunities.

Before Darwin put forward his theory of evolution by natural selection, it was accepted that each species that we see today had always existed precisely as we now see it. God had created each one, with all its detailed adaptations, and these had remained unchanged. Fossils were merely the remains of other types of animal, each equally unchanging during its span of existence, which God had destroyed in a catastrophe (or a number of catastrophes) such as the biblical Flood.

In his journey round the world in the ship H.M.S. *Beagle* from 1831 to 1836, Darwin saw two phenomena that eventually led him to disbelieve all this. On the Galápagos Islands in the Pacific, isolated from South America by 600 miles of sea, different birds were well adapted to feeding on different diets. Some, with heavy beaks, cracked open nuts or seeds; some, with smaller beaks, fed on fruit and flowers; others again, with fine, narrow beaks, fed on insects. On the mainland, these different niches are occupied by quite different, unrelated types of bird—for example, by toucans, parrots and flycatchers. The remarkable fact was that on the Galápagos Islands each of these varied niches was instead filled by a differently adapted species of one type of bird, the finch. It looked very much as though finches had managed to colonize the Galápagos Islands before other types of bird and then, free from their competition, had been able to adapt to diets and ways of life that were normally not available to them. This logical explanation, however, ran directly against the current idea of the fixity of characteristics. Equally disturbing were the fossils which Darwin had found in South America. The sloth, armadillo and guanaco (the wild ancestor of the domesticated llama) were each represented by fossils which were larger than the living forms, but were clearly very similar to them. Again, the idea that the living species were descended from the fossil species was a straightforward explanation, but one that contradicted the view that each species was a special creation and had no blood relationship with any other species.

Natural selection   The explanation that Darwin eventually deduced and published in 1858 is now an almost universally accepted part of the basic philosophy of biological science. Darwin realized that any pair of animals or plants produces far more offspring than would be needed simply to replace that pair: there must, therefore, be competition for survival amongst the offspring. Furthermore, these offspring are not identical with one another, but vary slightly in their characteristics. Inevitably, some of these variations will prove to be better adapted to the mode of life of the organism than others. The offspring which have these favourable characteristics will then have a natural advantage in the competition of life, and will tend to survive at the expense of their less fortunate relatives. By their survival, and eventual mating, this process of *natural selection* will lead to the persistence of these favourable characteristics into the next generation.

Evolution is therefore possible because of competition between individuals that differ slightly from one another. But why should these differences exist, and why should each species not be able to evolve a single, perfect answer to the demands that the environment makes upon it? All the flowers of a particular species of plant would then, for example, be of exactly the same colour, and every sparrow would have a beak of precisely the same size and shape. Such a simple solution is not possible, because the demands of the environment are neither stable nor uniform. Conditions vary from place to place, from day to day, from season to season. No single type can be the best possible adaptation to all these varying conditions. Instead, one particular size of beak might be the best for the winter diet of a sparrow, while another might be better adapted to its summer food. Since, during the lifetimes of two sparrows differing in this way, each type of beak is slightly better adapted at one time and slightly worse adapted at another, natural selection will not favour one at the expense of the other. Both types will therefore continue to exist in the population as a whole.

Because we do not normally examine sparrows very closely, we are not aware of the many ways in which the individual birds may differ from one another. In reality, of course, they vary in as many ways as do different individual human beings. In our own species, we are accustomed to the multitude of trivial variations that make each individual recognizably unique—the precise shape and size of the nose, ears, eyes, chin, mouth, teeth, the colour of the eyes and hair and the type of complexion, the texture and waviness of the hair; the height and build, the pitch of voice, and degree of resistance to different stresses and diseases. We know of other, less obvious characteristics in which individuals also differ, such as their fingerprints and their blood group. All of these variations are, then, the material upon which natural selection can act. In each generation, those individuals that carry the greatest number of less advantageous characteristics would be least likely to live long enough to have children who would perpetuate these traits, while those with a large number of more advantageous characteristics would be more likely to survive and breed successfully.

Changes of this kind in the characteristics of a species are not merely theoretical deductions, but can be shown to have taken place. This can be seen clearly only when the environment of a species has changed rapidly, which does happen, though rarely. A particularly clear example resulted from the darkening of the countryside around the industrial cities of Great Britain during the second half of the 19th century.[1] This change greatly affected those moths, such as the peppered moth, *Biston betularia,* which relied upon camouflage to protect them from being seen and eaten by insectivorous birds. As long as the bark of the trees on which they rested was pale, it was advantageous for the moths to be pale also. But as industrialization proceeded and the bark of trees near the cities became blackened by soot, the pale individuals of *B. betularia* were now more and more conspicuous (Fig. 4.1). It was no coincidence that it was in 1848 that a dark or 'melanic' form of this moth first appeared and gradually became more and more common in these industrial areas until, by 1895, it was the pale form which was now the rare exception near the cities. The reason for this change is quite clear. Against the soot-darkened bark it was now the melanic form which was less conspicuous and therefore favoured by natural selection. Experiments have confirmed this deduction. A large number of peppered moths, some light and some dark, each marked by a tiny spot of paint, were released in two areas. In the first, a non-industrial area, later trapping led to the recapture of 14·6 per cent of the pale coloured moths, but of only 4·7 per cent of the melanic forms—far more of these had already been eaten by birds. In the industrial area the proportions were reversed: only 14 per cent of the pale moths were recaptured, but 27·5 per cent of the dark forms, which here had been better camouflaged than their paler relatives. It is also interesting to find that, near towns which have in recent years taken measures to reduce smoke production, the proportion of melanic moths has already dropped.

This is not the only known example of a rapid change in the characteristics of an insect, due to the influence of man. The use of DDT to control insects conferred a great advantage upon those which were resistant to this chemical, and a high proportion of house flies are now of the DDT-resistant variety. The evolution of strains of bacteria resistant to commonly used antibiotics provides other clear examples of Darwin's principle of natural selection in action.

An interesting botanical parallel to this zoological response to industrial pollution is provided by the bent-grasses *Agrostis stolonifera* and *A. tenuis* living around a copper refinery that was established in northern England in about 1900.[2] The soil from uncontaminated grassland in the area contained less than 100 parts per million of copper; this grassland contained many species of plant, and samples of the two *Agrostis* species showed very little tolerance to higher levels of copper. At the other

Figure 4.1a. Photograph showing the inconspicuousness of the normal form and the conspicuous appearance of the melanic form of the peppered moth (*Biston betularia*) on an unpolluted, lichen-covered tree trunk in Dorset, England. (From the experiments of Bernard Kettlewell, University of Oxford.)

extreme, old-established lawns near the refinery were composed exclusively of *A. stolonifera* and *A. tenuis*, and these were living in soils containing 2600–4200 p.p.m. of copper. Interestingly enough, some lawns that had been established in the last 10 years, in which the soil contains 1900–4800 p.p.m. of copper, bore a greater variety of species of grass, and the species of *Agrostis* showed a lower mean level of tolerance. This suggests that the process of selection of copper-tolerant forms is still taking place in these small populations.

If all the members of a species gradually came to possess such new characters as a resistance to DDT, the species would have changed but no additional species would have resulted. However, as Darwin realized in

Figure 4.1b. The reverse situation when the same forms are on a soot-covered trunk near Birmingham, England. (From the experiments of Bernard Kettlewell, University of Oxford.)

the Galápagos Islands, the original single species may also split into two or more new species. In order to explain how this happens, the meaning of the term 'species' must first be explained. Why do biologists consider that a sparrow and a robin are separate species, but that an alsatian and a greyhound (which appear just as different from one another) are both members of the same species? To biologists, the essential difference is that, under normal conditions in the wild, a sparrow and a robin do not mate together, while an alsatian and a greyhound will (the great difference in the appearance of the two dogs is due to artificial selection by man). Sometimes the difference is a little more subtle, as in the case of the horse and the ass; though these are separate species, they do sometimes breed together. However, this cross between the two species is short-lived and genetic change may be, each is likely to reappear in a certain percentage of the population as a whole. In a larger population, each mutation or recombination will therefore reappear sufficiently often that the effects of random chance are nullified, and the underlying advantages or disadvantages that they confer will eventually show themselves as increased or decreased reproductive success. For this reason, it is the population, and not the individual, that is the real unit of evolutionary change.

The way in which the genotype is expressed, as the morphology, physiology, behaviour, etc., of the organism, is known as the *phenotype*. This is somewhat variable and can be modified by the environment. Thus, identical twins (sharing therefore an identical genotype) will come to differ from one another if they are brought up in areas with, for example, differing amounts of sunlight or of available food. This slight plasticity of the genotype is valuable from an evolutionary point of view, for it makes it possible for a single genotype to survive in slightly different habitats. In each habitat, natural selection can then act on its descendants, which may in this way eventually become genotypically adapted to that environment.

External isolating forces   It is, then, the independent appearance of new mutations in each population, and the independent course of genetic change within populations, that together make up the driving force within the organism which tends to make each isolated population gradually become different from every other. The force *outside* the organism that aids the process is simpler. Natural selection acts to adapt the population to its surroundings. But no two patches of woodland, no two freshwater ponds, will be absolutely identical, even if they lie in the same area of country. They may differ in the precise nature of their soil or water, in their range of temperature, or their average temperature, or in the particular species of animal or plant that may become unusually rare or unusually common in that locality. Since each population has to adapt to slightly different conditions, the two populations will gradually come to differ from one another.

The history of a patch of sunflowers living in a ditch in the Sacramento Valley of California provides a good example of the way in which all these forces can gradually make two populations become quite different from one another.[3] The population consisted of natural hybrids between the annual sunflowers of California, *Helianthus annuus* and *H. bolanderi*. To begin with, the original population gradually became split into two by a drying-out of part of the ditch, the dry section being colonized by grasses among which the sunflowers could not survive. Over the space of five years, the dry grassy patch widened until it had pushed the two separated sub-populations of sunflowers over 100 metres apart. One of these was now in a deeper part of the ditch, which remained wet until late spring, while the other grew in a shallower, drier position. The two sub-populations became different in a number of characteristics, such as the shape of the flower head as a whole, the number of sterile floret rays surrounding the head, the shape of the base of the leaf, and the length of the hairs on the stem and leaves. Even though bees could easily fly from one population to the other, so that some cross-pollination between them must have taken place, observations over the next seven years showed that the differences between the two populations did not disappear. Their environments differed sufficiently to preserve the distinctiveness of the two populations.

Exactly the same process takes place in animal populations though, because they can move, the separate populations may each cover a larger area. For example, two species of Carpenter Bee, *Xylocopa diversipes* and *X. nobilis*, live in the large East Indian island of Celebes.[4] Three different colour patterns of each species are known on Celebes, each making up one or more separate populations. Another three colour patterns of *X. nobilis* are known to exist on neighbouring islets (Fig. 4.2).

Once populations have started to diverge in their genetic adaptations in this way, the foundations for the appearance of a new species have been laid. If two divergent populations should meet again when the process has not gone very far, they may completely hybridize and merge into one another. The further, vital step towards the appearance of a new species is when hybrids between the two independent populations do appear, but only along a narrow zone where the two populations meet. Such a situation suggests that, though continued interbreeding within this zone can

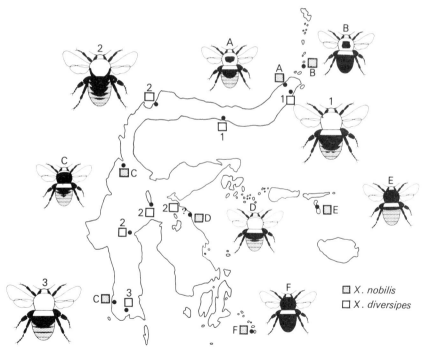

Figure 4.2. Colour patterns of two species of carpenter bee, *Xylocopa nobilis* (A-F) and *X. diversipes* (1–3) on the East Indian island of Celebes and neighbouring islets. Three separate populations of each species occur on the main island, each with distinct patterning. A further three pattern types of *X. nobilis* occur on the surrounding islets.

produce a population of hybrids, these hybrids cannot compete elsewhere with either of the pure parent populations. This seems to be the situation with the woodpecker-like flickers of North America. The eastern yellow-shafted flicker, *Colaptes auratus,* does mate with the western red-shafted flicker, *C. cafer,* along a narrow 2000-mile-long stretch where the two meet, but this zone of hybridization does not seem to be spreading (Fig. 4.3).

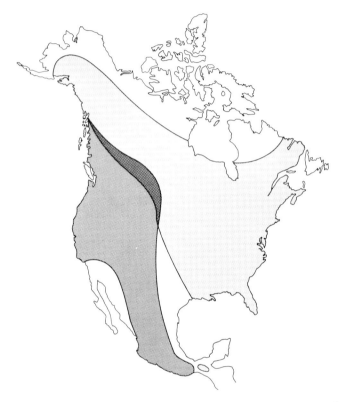

Figure 4.3. The yellow-shafted flicker of eastern and north-western North America hybridizes with the red-shafted flicker of the south-west over a long but narrow zone.

Barriers to interbreeding   Once independent evolution in isolation has produced a situation in which the hybrids are less well-adapted than either of their parents, then natural selection will favour individuals that do not perpetuate this more poorly adapted hybrid population. This may be either because they cannot, or will not, mate with individuals from the other group, or because such unions are infertile. The barrier to hybridization is known as an *isolating mechanism,* and it may take many forms. In animals such as birds and insects, that have complicated courtship and mating behaviour, small differences in these rituals may in themselves effectively prevent interbreeding. Sometimes the preference for the mating site may differ slightly. For example, the North American toads

Bufo fowleri and *B. americanus* live in the same areas, but breed in different places.[5] *B. fowleri* breeds in large, still bodies of water such as ponds, large rainpools and quiet streams, whereas *B. americanus* prefers shallow puddles or brook pools. Interbreeding between species is also hindered by the fact that *B. americanus* breeds in early spring and *B. fowleri* in the late spring—though there is some mid-spring overlap.

Many flowering plants are pollinated by animals that are attracted to the flowers by their nectar or pollen. Hybridization may then be prevented by the adaptation of the flowers to different pollinators. For example, differences in size, shape and colour of the flowers of related species of the North American beard-tongue (*Pentstemon*) adapt them to pollination by different insects—or, in one case, by a humming-bird (Fig. 4.4). In other

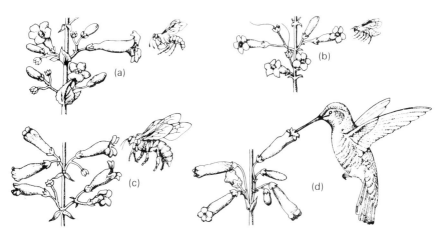

Figure 4.4. Four species of the beard-tongue (*Pentstemon*) found in California, together with their pollinators. Species (a) and (b) are pollinated by solitary wasps, species (c) by carpenter bees, and species (d) by hummingbirds. (After Stebbins.[6])

plants, related species have come to differ in the time at which they shed their pollen, thus making hybridization impossible. Even if pollen of another species does reach the stigma of a flower, in many cases it is unable even to form a pollen-tube, because the biochemical environment in which it finds itself is too alien. It cannot, therefore, grow down to fertilize the ovum. Similarly, in many animals alien spermatozoa cause an allergy reaction in the walls of the female genital passage and the spermatozoa subsequently die before fertilization.

Other isolating mechanisms may not prevent mating and fertilization taking place, but instead ensure that the union is sterile. These may be genetic isolating mechanisms, the structure and arrangement of the genes on the chromosomes being so different that the normal processes of chromosome splitting and pairing that accompany cell division are disrupted. These differences may make themselves felt at any stage from the time of fertilization of the ovum, through all the steps in development, to that its chemicals remain isolated from those of its surroundings, and that it remains within the range of conditions in which its own chemicals can continue to function. Evolutionary history has been the gradual process by which organisms have become able to isolate themselves (or, more precisely, their body tissues) from their surroundings with increasing effectiveness. This has made it possible for organisms to become able to survive in conditions that are more and more unfavourable for life—the conquest of dry land being a major step in that direction.

Alongside the evolution of adaptations providing insulation from the physical environment, organisms have also had to cope with difficulties due to their companion species. Both the existence of animals or plants that are similar to one another in their adaptations, and which therefore compete with one another, and the complicated interactions of herbivore and plant food or of predator and prey, lead to the appearance of new difficulties. Evolution is, therefore, the process by which organisms have conquered two types of barrier: those imposed by physical conditions, and those resulting from the biological world of animals and plants among which they live.

Even in the most favourable habitats, the physical conditions are rarely ideal for the organism through the 24-hour daily cycle. In addition to the daily alteration of light and dark, with the accompanying rise and fall in temperature and relative humidity, the temperature and rainfall may vary considerably from one day to another in many areas. Any organism must be able to tolerate changes of this kind in the physical conditions: animals may take shelter during rainstorms, while plants may close their leaves or flowers.

As long as these conditions are short-lived, evasion or toleration is not difficult. A more serious problem exists in parts of the world where the climate is seasonal. Here the conditions may not be severe in themselves, but their continuation over a period of months demands a quite different adaptation on the part of the organism. Such prolonged alterations in physical conditions inevitably affect the whole community: the lower temperatures and shorter daylight hours of winter directly affect both plants and animals and, in addition, most animals find that food is then far less plentiful. Some animals, of course, are able to avoid these conditions altogether, by migrating to warmer climates. This solution is particularly common in flying animals, such as birds and butterflies, that can cover relatively long distances with ease, and to which a river or a stretch of sea is not an impassable obstacle. Other animals, such as bears and many smaller mammals, endure the cold and the scarcity of food by *hibernating*—reducing their metabolism to a minimum and surviving on food reserves they have stored up in the body during the summer. Resting stages, of one kind or another, are common in both animals and plants of higher latitudes. The hard, resistant seed-cases of many plants, which will not germinate until they have been exposed to the coldness of winter (during which the parent plant may die), have their counterpart in the periods of arrested development of many insects. The hard, resistant chrysalis of a butterfly is a stage during which the complex changes from the caterpillar to the winged adult are carried out. But this inert, non-feeding stage is equally a convenient form in which, by a slowing-down of the rate of these changes, the whole winter can be passed in comparative safety.

For plants, the dry season of areas closer to the Equator brings the risk of desiccation due to lack of water, which may also be unavailable during winter in cold-temperate latitudes because it is frozen into ice. Winter also brings the danger of frost damage. Though the stem of the plant can be protected by bark, the leaves are still exposed. The flowering plants were able to solve this problem by developing the mechanism of leaf-fall, so that the enormous, exposed leaf-surface is shed completely until the following spring. It is interesting to find that this adaptation was probably first developed by flowering plants in the tropical regions to reduce water loss during the dry season.[9] Only later did flowering plants with this *deciduous* habit spread to the colder regions where water is also in short supply because it is frozen. In addition to cutting down the rate of water loss, the reduction in the exposed surface area, due to the shedding of leaves in winter, reduces the damage caused by high winds and by settling snow in these regions.

Meeting the challenge of the environment   The adaptations considered so far are all ones that in one way or another *evaded* the challenge of inhospitable conditions. To live and carry on all its normal functions in an area that is particularly cold, or particularly hot and dry, requires a more thoroughgoing adaptation of the whole organization of the organism and of its life-history. For example, most frogs and toads cannot survive in desert regions because the adults quickly become desiccated and because the water that the embryos need for their development rapidly becomes too hot for their existence and eventually evaporates completely. Nevertheless, some frogs and toads have been able to adapt to these conditions. An example is the spadefoot toad *Scaphiopus couchii* which is found in the deserts of the south-western United States.[10] Its eggs are laid in temporary desert rainpools resulting from local storms, and their rate of development is very high. As a result, they pass through the most temperature-sensitive stages of their development before the afternoon of the next day, when the temperature rises above the level (about 34°C) that is critical for them. The larvae also hatch at an early stage from the mass of jelly which surrounds them and are therefore soon able to seek the coolest parts of the rainpool. The adults can survive in these deserts because their hind limbs are modified to form scoop-like spades, with which they can excavate holes. In the hottest periods they can therefore retreat from the desert surface to the cooler, moister environment of their hole.

Even the spadefoot toad is, in retreating to its hole, still only temporarily able to evade the problems posed by the physical conditions of its environment; it will eventually have to emerge to feed. The limitations of this type of solution are as obvious as are the advantages of more fundamental adaptations that permanently insulate the organism from unfavourable physical conditions. The insulating coat, formed by hair in there are daily visual or vocal displays of the whole population, especially at dawn or dusk. Some ecologists have suggested that this is a method by which the population of a species becomes aware of its own density.[14] If this is unduly high, this might lead to physiological or behavioural changes, such as a reduction in the number of individuals that mate, or a reduction in the number of eggs laid, which could eventually reduce the size of the population. The absence of a system of this kind in our own species may well be one of the reasons why our numbers have so enormously increased that we now threaten to overwhelm the resources of our planet.

References

1 KETTLEWELL H.B.D. (1961) The phenomenon of industrial melanism in Lepidoptera. *Ann. Rev. Entomol.* **6**, 245–262.

2 LIN WU & BRADSHAW A.D. (1972) Aerial pollution and the rapid evolution of copper tolerance. *Nature, Lond.* **238**, 167–169.

3 STEBBINS G.L. & DALY K. (1961) Changes in the variation pattern of a hybrid population of *Helianthus* over an eight year period. *Evolution* **15**, 60–61.

4 VAN DER VECHT J. (1953) The carpenter bees (*Xylocopa* Latr.) of Celebes. *Idea* **9**, 57–59.

5 BLAIR A.P. (1942) Isolating mechanisms in a complex of four species of toads. *Biol. Symp.* **6**, 235–249.

6 STEBBINS G.L. (1950)*Variation and Evolution in Plants.* Columbia University Press, New York.

7 MAYR E. (1970) *Populations, Species and Evolution.* Oxford University Press, London.

8 WILLIS J.C. (1922) *Age and Area.* Cambridge University Press, Cambridge.

9 AXELROD D.I. (1966) Origin of deciduous and evergreen habits in temperate forests. *Evolution* **20**, 1–15.

10 ZWEIFEL R.G. (1968) Reproductive biology of anurans of the arid South-West, with emphasis on adaptation of embryos to temperature. *Bull. Am. Mus. nat. Hist.* **140**, 1–64.

11 JAMES F.C. (1970) Geographic size variations in birds and its relationship to climate. *Ecology* **51**, 365–390.

12 EHRLICH P.R. & RAVEN P.H. (1964) Butterflies and plants: a study in co-evolution. *Evolution* **18**, 586–608.

13 WATSON A. (1977) Population limitation and the adaptive value of territorial behaviour in the Scottish red grouse *Lagopus l. scoticus*. In: Stonehouse B. and Perrins C. (eds). *Evolutionary Ecology*, pp. 19–26. Macmillan, London.

14 WYNNE-EDWARDS V.C. (1962) *Animal Dispersion in Relation to Social Behaviour.* Oliver & Boyd, Edinburgh and London.

CHAPTER 5

LIFE (AND DEATH) ON ISLANDS

As we have seen in Chapter 4, isolation is one of the key factors in permitting evolutionary change, for it allows the gene pool of a population to become different from that of other populations. On large land-masses, that isolation is variable in its nature and therefore in its effects on the biota as a whole. Islands provide clearer examples of isolation, for the sea surrounding them is an environment in which few terrestrial or freshwater organisms can survive for any length of time. Special adaptations for transport by air or water are necessary for an organism to cross a stretch of ocean. Dispersal to islands is therefore by a sweepstakes route, the successful organisms sharing adaptations for crossing the intervening region rather than for living within it (see p. 6). This greatly restricts the diversity of life that is capable of emigrating to an island. But, as we shall see, many factors control precisely how many organisms will reach and colonize an island, and also control the degree of diversity that its biota will ultimately attain. By comparing the biotas of islands of different size, or islands lying at different distances from their source of colonists, or islands of different topography or lying at different latitudes, we can learn much about the interaction of these factors in the control of organic diversity.

Islands are therefore of interest in three ways. Firstly, it is interesting to a biologist to observe the nature of the island biota: how it differs from that of its source-area, and the nature of the adaptations of the immigrants that allowed them to reach and to colonize the island. Secondly, it is interesting to attempt to identify and quantify the factors that control three phenomena: the rate at which new species reach an island, the rate at which species become extinct on an island, and the number of species that an island can support. Thirdly, it is interesting to study the processes of evolutionary change by which the island biota becomes an integrated ecosystem, each organism adapted to the physical and biological aspects of its life on the island, while some groups diversify to occupy ecological niches that on the mainland are normally occupied by other groups. After discussing these aspects of island biology and giving some examples of each, their interaction is examined by discussing the biota of the Hawaiian Islands.

Problems of access   Oceans are the most effective barrier to the distribution of all land animals except those that can fly. Some flying animals, such as larger birds and bats, may be capable of reaching even the most distant islands unaided, using their own powers of flight, especially if, like water birds, they are able to alight on the surface of the water to rest

An example of the relative importance of these different methods of plant dispersal is provided by the Galápagos Islands.[2] Nearly all of the *indigenous* flora of these islands (i.e. those not introduced by man) is derived from that of South America, and about 378 colonizations were probably involved. Birds probably brought 60 per cent of these, 31 per cent were wind-dispersed, and 9 per cent drifted in by sea.

Variety of island habitats   Islands smaller than about 9 hectares are effectively no more than beaches, because they are incapable of holding fresh water, and the flora is therefore restricted to species that are salt tolerant.[3] This leads to a corresponding reduction in the variety of animal life. The inhospitability of the beach is merely an extreme example of the problem that faces any organism, even after it has succeeded in reaching an island. This is the problem of finding a habitat in which it can survive. It is obvious that a large island is more likely to contain a greater variety of habitats than a smaller one, and that it will therefore be able to support a greater variety of forms of life. For example, studies of islands off the coast of California and Baja California have shown that their area is the most important single factor in determining the diversity of their flowering plant populations.[4] Though the diversity of available habitats also increases in islands that include higher ground, providing a cooler, moister climate, these studies showed that this factor appeared to have comparatively little effect. The effects of latitude were, however, detectable.

The very great importance of the diversity of habitat available can be shown by comparing the bat faunas of a number of islands off the northern coast of South America. Aruba, Curaçao and Bonaire, which are arid, have few species, and only one more is found in Margarita, which has little rain-forest. The numbers increase considerably in Grenada, Tobago and Trinidad, where there are great areas of rain-forest, and especially in Trinidad, which also has some mountains.

Problems of isolation   In this last example, getting to the islands was not a great problem, since bats can readily fly from island to island. In most cases, however, the biota is strongly affected by the degree of isolation of the island. However diverse the habitats that it offers, the variety of the

Figure 5.2. The distribution of conifers and flowering plants in the Pacific Islands. The first number beside each island group is the total number of genera found there; the second is the number of endemic genera found there. B, Bismarck Archipelago; C, Cook Islands; E, Easter Island; EC, East Carolines; F, Fiji Islands; H, Hawaiian Islands; LPT, Line, Phoenix and Tokelau Island groups; M, Marquesas; N, Norfolk Island; NC, New Caledonia; NG, New Guinea; NH, New Hebrides; NT, Northern Tuamotu Islands; NZ, New Zealand; Ph, Philippines; R, Rapa Island; Sa, Samoa group; Soc, Society Islands; Sol, Solomon Islands; ST, Southern Tuamotu Islands; StC, Santa Cruz Islands; T, Tonga group; Tub, Tubai group; WC, West Carolines. (Data from Van Balgooy, 1971.[5])

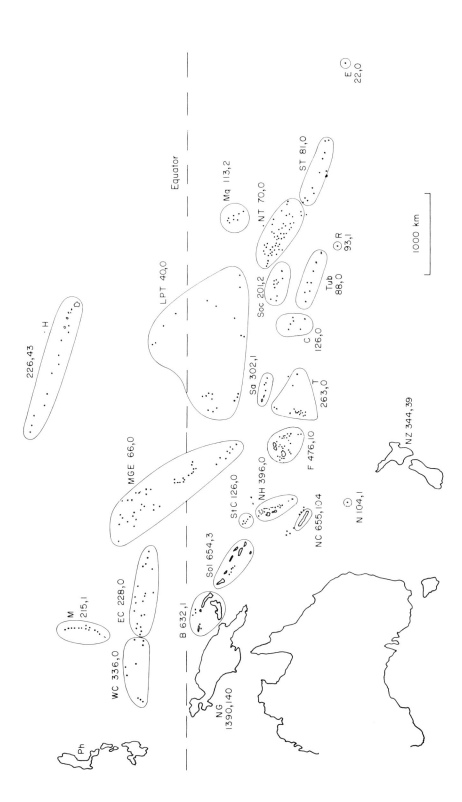

226,43

·H

M
215,1

WC 336,0

EC 228,0

Ph

NG
1390,140

B 632,1

Sol 654,3

N 104,1

MGE 66,0

StC 126,0

NH 396,0

NC 655,104

F 476,10

NZ 344,39

LPT 40,0

Sa 302,1

T
263,0

C
126,0

Soc 201,2

Tub
88,0

R
93,1

Mq 113,2

NT 70,0

ST 81,0

E
22,0

Equator

1000 km

Finally, small populations are also far more susceptible to random non-adaptive changes in their genetic make-up. Since it is less likely to be closely adapted to its environment, a small population is also more liable to chance extinction.

A species which can make use of a wide variety of food is therefore at an advantage on an island, for its maximum possible population size will be greater than that of a species with more restricted food preferences. The advantage of this will be especially great in a small island, in which the possible population sizes are in any case smaller. This is probably the reason why, for example, though on the larger islands of the Galápagos group both the medium-sized finch *Geospiza fortis* and the small *G. fuliginosa* can co-exist, on some of the smaller islands of the group there is only a single form of intermediate size.[9]

The effects of both island area and species habitat-tolerance have been demonstrated by the American ecologist Kenneth Crowell, who introduced two species of vole to nine small islands in Penobscot Bay, Maine, and studied their success or failure over the following 10 years.[10] The voles became extinct on the two smallest islands, and on those with the smallest areas of the dense herb cover that provided a suitable environment for them. The red-backed vole (*Clethrionomys gapperi*) was also less successful than the meadow vole (*Microtus pennsylvanicus*), perhaps because the former is found in a more restricted variety of habitats, although it is also possible that it was not able to compete successfully with *Microtus*.

Chance extinction is also a particular danger for the predators in the fauna, since their numbers must always be far lower than those of the species upon which they prey. As a result, island faunas tend to be unbalanced in their composition, containing fewer varieties of predator than a similar mainland area. This in turn reinforces the fundamental lack of variety of the animal and plant life of an island, which is due to the hazards involved in entry and colonization. The complex interactions of continental communities containing a rich and varied fauna and flora act as a buffer that can cope with occasional fluctuations in the density of different species, and even with temporary local extinction of a species. This resilience is lacking in the simple island community, and so the chance extinction of one species may have serious effects and lead to the extinction of other species. All these factors increase the rate at which island species may become extinct.

There are clearly several different possible reasons why a particular organism may be absent from a particular island. It may be unable to reach it; it may reach it but be unable to colonize it; it may have colonized it but later have become extinct, or it may simply as yet, by chance, not have reached the island.[11] It is often very difficult to decide which of these possible reasons was the cause in any particular case. In some instances, as for example where two species have complementary distributions in the same island group but are never found on the same island, the facts obviously suggest that they compete with one another so strongly that they cannot co-exist.

The theory of island biogeography   The number of species found on an island, therefore, depends on a number of factors—not only its area and topography, its diversity of habitats, its accessibility from the source of its colonists, and the richness of that source, but also the equilibrium between the rate of colonization by new species and the rate of extinction of existing species. Many individual observations and analyses of such phenomena have been made over the past 150 years. However, only recently have biologists attempted to synthesize these into quantitative theoretical models that can be used to predict the likely results of particular sets of conditions. This culminated in the book by Robert MacArthur and Edward Wilson, *The Theory of Island Biogeography*, in which this mathematical approach is clearly explained.[12]

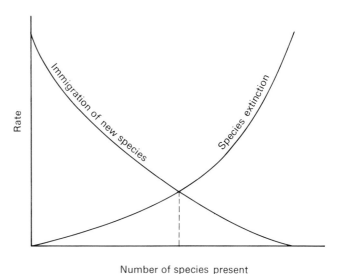

Figure 5.5. Equilibrium model of the biota of a single island. The equilibrium number of species, indicated by the dashed line, is reached at the intersection point between the curve of rate of immigration of new species, not already on the island, and the curve of extinction of species on the island. (After MacArthur and Wilson, 1967.[7])

Initially, they simply show how the position of the equilibrium point depends on the balance between the rates of colonization and of extinction (Fig. 5.5). The rate of colonization will be high initially, because the island will be reached quickly by those species that are adept at dispersal, and because these will all be new to the island. As time passes, more and more immigrants will belong to species that have already colonized the island, so that the rate of appearance of new species will drop. The rate of extinction, on the other hand, will rise. This is partly because, since every species runs the risk of extinction, the more that have arrived, the more species there are at risk. In addition, as more species arrive, the average population size of each will diminish as competition increases.

At first, the few species present can occupy a greater variety of ecological niches than would be possible on the mainland, where they are competing with many other species. For example, in the comparison mentioned earlier (p. 123) between the Panama mainland and Puercos Island, the smaller number of bird species in the island were able, because of reduced competition, to be far more abundant: there were 1·35 pairs per species per hectare in Puercos Island, compared with only 0·33 and 0·28, respectively, for the two mainland areas.[8] This effect of release from competition was especially noticeable in the antshrike (*Thamnophilus doliatus*). On the mainland, where it competed with over 20 other species of ant-eating bird, there were only 8 pairs of antshrike per 40 hectares; on Puercos Island, where there was only one such competitor, there were 112 pairs of antshrike per 40 hectares.

If an island is later colonized by a new species which makes use of foodstuffs similar to those consumed by one of the earlier immigrants, competition between the two species will take place. As in the case of the closely related populations discussed in Chapter 4, this may result in the extinction of one of the two competitors, or in the gradual divergence of their food preferences so that the extent to which they are competing with one another is reduced. This latter process, the temporal or spatial separation of species described in Chapter 3, has the result that each is becoming more specialized in its requirements, making better use of a smaller variety of the possible sources of nourishment. For example, though three different insectivorous species of the tanager (*Tanagra*) co-exist on the island of Trinidad, competition between them is reduced because they hunt for insects on different parts of the vegetation: *T. guttata* searches mainly on the leaves, *T. gyrola* on the large twigs and *T. mexicana* mainly on the smaller twigs.[13] If the variety of food used by each species is reduced in this way, it must follow that the size of the population of each species that the island can support is now smaller. Since the chances of extinction are greater for smaller populations, the rate of extinction must rise as new species colonize the island, until the equilibrium point is reached at which the rates of colonization and of extinction are equal.

In some situations the rate of extinction may not increase as rapidly as in MacArthur and Wilson's model. For example, if the island initially contained no fauna or flora at all, there will be a gradual progression through a number of seral stages to the climax community. At each stage, some immigrants that would previously have been unable to establish themselves will now, for the first time, find a vacant niche. These changes may also, of course, lead to some extinctions among the earlier colonizing species.

As outlined above, the biotic equilibrium point will also depend upon the size of the island, and on its distance from the source of its colonists. MacArthur and Wilson show this, also, in graphic form (Fig. 5.6). They also give a mathematical analysis of the interaction of these factors, which predicts quite high rates of extinction.

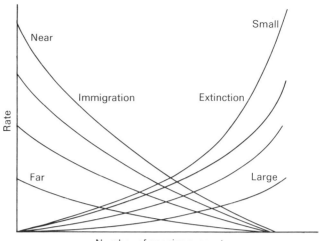

Figure 5.6. The inter-relationship between isolation and area is determining the equilibrium point of biotic diversity. Increasing distance of the island from its source of colonists lowers the rate of immigration (left). Increasing area lowers the rate of extinction (right). (After MacArthur and Wilson, 1967.[12])

Such mathematical studies of the equilibrium level of species diversity in islands are not of only academic interest. They tell us much about the likely rates of species turnover in any isolated environment, and they are therefore of considerable importance to efforts to conserve biotas or individual species, especially in wild-life preserves or national parks, which may in many ways be regarded as islands. These topics are discussed further in Chapter 9 (see p. 226).

Evidence for biotic equilibrium   Though evidence from comparing the biotas of different islands may suggest that they differ in their extinction rates or their immigration rates, and therefore in the potential diversity of their biotas, other studies provide more direct evidence on the validity of these interpretations. These studies are of the colonization of islands devoid of life, or of islands which have changed in area or have only recently been severed from the mainland.

The most famous natural example of the destruction of a biota and its subsequent re-establishment followed the explosion of the island volcano Mount Krakatoa in 1883. By 1908, 13 species of bird had colonized the island. When further collections were made in 1919–21, the total of bird species had risen to 31, but two of the species found in 1908 were not collected or seen. By 1932–34, the total number of species (30) had remained almost stable, suggesting that this represents the equilibrium number for the island, but five species found previously were now absent. These figures suggest a rate of extinction of 0·2–0·4 species per year, i.e. that one species becomes extinct every 2–5 years—and the real figure may be higher than this, since it may be that a species could become extinct and reappear by recolonization between one collection period and the next. The figures are not very different from the extinction rate of 0·8–1·6 species per year predicted by MacArthur and Wilson's mathematical analysis. However, Williams'[14] studies on the ecology of colonization by the iguanid lizard *Anolis* in the West Indies suggests that extinction rates of terrestrial animals may be lower, since new waves of immigration, leading to competition and extinction, are far less frequent than in birds.

More detailed studies of the progress of island colonization have recently been made by Dan Simberloff and Edward Wilson, who fumigated four small islets in Florida Bay to remove the insect population.[15] These studies showed that the rates of insect colonization and extinction of an islet 200 m from its source area were quite high, resulting in a turnover rate of one species every 1–2 days (the original insect fauna having been between 20 and 50 species, out of a total insect fauna of several hundreds in the Florida Keys area). The insect fauna of the islands had returned to the original level within about 6 months and, although further colonization and extinction continued thereafter, the number of insect species did not change significantly. This return to the original level of insect diversity (Fig. 5.7) was despite the fact that only 25–30 per cent of the original species were present in the island faunas 1 year after defaunation. This experiment therefore not only demonstrated a high rate of colonization and extinction, but also supported the theory that there was a certain equilibrium level of diversity to which the fauna of the islets returned, and that this was not merely a resultant of the particular assemblage of species that had originally been present.

The post-glacial rise in sea-levels has also created a number of new islands by flooding the low-lying margins of continents, any hills now appearing as islands surrounded by sea. Since, as we have seen, the equilibrium diversity of an island biota is less than that of a similar

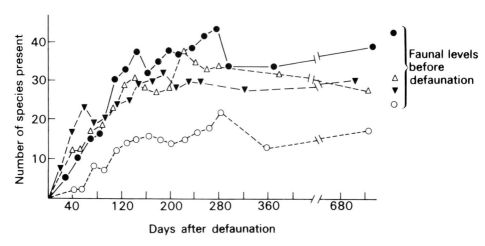

Figure 5.7. The colonization curves of four small mangrove islets in the Florida Keys. (After Simberloff and Wilson, 1970.[15])

Life (and Death) on Islands

mainland area, it would be expected that these islands would, when they were created, have a 'supersaturated' biota. This would gradually diminish, so that older islands should have moved further towards the biotic equilibrium appropriate to their area. This has been shown to be true for the lizard faunas of 17 islands off the coast of Baja California, which had become isolated by the rising sea-levels at various times from 6000 to 12 000 years ago.[16]

Impermanent islands These studies of islands that have changed in area, or that have become islands only comparatively recently, provide a useful reminder that islands are not static, unchanging areas of land. Biogeographers used to divide them into 'continental islands' or 'oceanic islands' according to whether they had, or had not, ever been part of a continental mass. This seemed a simple judgement to make when it was only changes in sea-level that were thought to have been responsible for the creation or disappearance of islands: only islands lying on a continental shelf could ever have been linked to the mainland. Now that it is realized that continental drift, too, has caused the fragmentation of continental masses and their movement to new positions, the distinction is more difficult to make. Depending on the time of origin of a group of organisms, a particular area may have been either a part of a continent, an easily accessible offshore island, or a distant, almost inaccessible island. Even the source of its colonists may change, as in the case of New Guinea, which appears to have received its mammalian colonists from Australia but its tropical flowering plants from south-east Asia (see p. 165 and p. 178). In any case, the term 'island' is itself only a comparative term; Madagascar is an island if compared to the African mainland, but is effectively the mainland if viewed as the source of colonists for more distant islands such as Réunion or Mauritius.

Opportunities for adaptive radiation Colonists may encounter many difficulties when they first enter an island, but there are rich opportunities for those species that can survive them long enough for evolution to adapt them to the new environment. These opportunities exist because of the lack of many of the parasites and predators that elsewhere would prey upon the species, and of many of the other species with which it normally competes. Like Darwin's finches on the Galápagos Islands, it may be able to radiate into ways of life not formerly available to it.

A good example of this can be found in the Dry Tortugas, the islands off the extreme end of the Florida Keys, which only a few species of ant have successfully colonized.[12] One species, *Paratrechina longicornis*, on the mainland normally nests only in open environments under, or in the shelter of, large objects; but on the Dry Tortugas it also nests in environments such as tree trunks and open soil, which on the mainland are occupied by other species. Not every species, however, is capable of taking

All these organisms evolved in islands to fill habitats normally closed to them. But other evolutionary changes frequently found on islands are the direct result of the island environment itself, not of the restricted fauna and flora. We have seen how serious may be the effect of a small population. But the same island will be able to support a larger population of the same animal if the size of each individual is reduced. This evolutionary tendency on islands is shown by the find of fossil pygmy elephants that once lived on islands in both the Mediterranean and the East Indies. On a much smaller scale, the size of lizards on four of the Canary Islands still shows the same phenomenon. The head to vent length of males of the lizard *Lacerta galloti* ranges from 135 mm on the largest island, Tenerife, to only 82 mm on Hierro, the smallest.

Another tendency is for island species to lose the very dispersal mechanisms that allowed them to reach their home. Once on the restricted area of the island, the ability for long-distance dispersal is no longer of value to the species: in fact it is a disadvantage. The seeds of plants tend to lose their 'wings' or feathery tufts, and many island insects are wingless. The loss of wings by some island birds may be partly for this reason, and partly because there are often no predators from which to escape. A few out of many examples are the kiwi and moa of New Zealand, the elephant birds of Madagascar, and the dodo of Mauritius (the last three are extinct, but only because man was the predator).

The Hawaiian Islands   As has been seen, there are many aspects of island life that are unique, and many others that differ only in degree from life on the continental land masses. The result of the action of all these different factors can be seen by examining the flora and fauna of one particular group of islands. The Hawaiian Islands provide an excellent example, for they form an isolated chain, 2650 km long, lying in the middle of the North Pacific, just inside the Tropics (Fig. 5.9). Sherwin Carlquist has provided an interesting account of the islands and of their fauna and flora, pointing out the significance of many of the adaptations found there.[18]

The islands are of volcanic origin, rising steeply from a sea-floor which is 5500 m deep, to the volcanic peaks which reach up to 4250 m. Hawaii itself lies 3200 km from North America and 5500 km from Japan. The islands seem to be the result of the activity of a particular point in the Earth's interior, past which the sea-floor has been moving westwards as the Pacific plate moves in that direction (see Chapter 6 and Fig. 6.5). The most easterly, Hawaii, is therefore the youngest (less than 700 000 years old) and bears the still active volcanoes Kilauea and Mauna Loa. The most westerly island still visible, Kure, is about 15 million years old, but the Emperor Seamount chain, consisting of the remains of other islands now eroded to below sea-level, extends further westwards and then northwards to near the Kamchatka peninsula of Siberia. The oldest of these submerged seamounts is over 70 million years old, so that there must have been a group of islands in the north-central Pacific for at least this length of time.

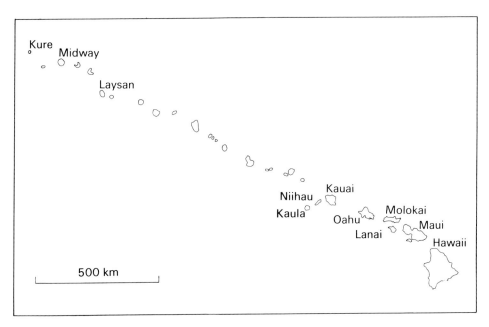

Figure 5.9. The Hawaiian Island chain.

It is clear that animals and plants have been able to colonize islands in this region for a very long period of time. Once arrived, they have been able to diversify and, often, to spread to the newly formed additions to the chain as the older islands steadily eroded away and disappeared beneath the sea. The high volcanic peaks seem to be islands within islands, for it is difficult for their alpine plants to disperse from one island to another. Instead, they have evolved from the adjacent lower-lying flora of each island: 91 per cent of the alpine plants of Hawaii are endemic, a far higher proportion than that of the island flora as a whole (16·5 per cent) or even of the angiosperms alone (20 per cent).[19]

The most obvious result of the extreme isolation of the Hawaiian Islands is that many groups are completely absent. There are no truly freshwater fish and no native amphibians, reptiles or mammals (except for one species of bat). The difficulty of getting to the islands is shown by the fact that the present-day bird fauna of Hawaii seems to be the result of only 15 different colonizations.

Most of the birds are of American origin, but the closest relatives of most of the Hawaiian animals and plants live in the Indo-Malaysian region. For example, of the 1729 species and varieties of Hawaiian seed plants, 40 per cent are of Indo-Malaysian origin but only 18 per cent are of American origin; also, nearly half of the 168 species of Hawaiian ferns have Indo-Malaysian relatives, but only 12 per cent have American affinities. This is not surprising, for the area to the east is almost completely empty while that to the south and west of the Hawaiian chain contains many islands, which can act as intermediary homes for migrants. Organisms

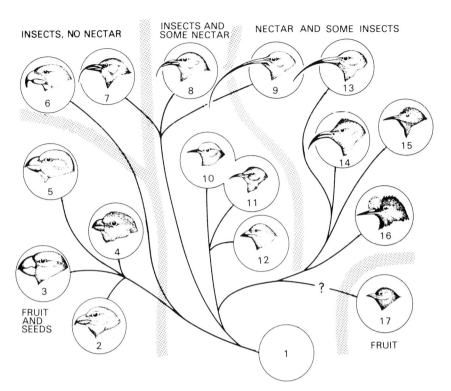

INSECTS, NO NECTAR   INSECTS AND SOME NECTAR   NECTAR AND SOME INSECTS

6 7 8 9 13 15 14 5 10 11 16 4 12

3

FRUIT AND SEEDS   2   1   ?   17   FRUIT

Figure 5.12. The evolution of dietary adaptations in the beaks of Hawaiian honey-creepers. 1, unknown finch-like colonist from North America. 2–5, *Psittacirostra psittacea, P. kona, P. bailleui, P. cantans.* 6, *Pseudonestor xanthophrys.* 7–9, *Hemignathus wilsoni, H. lucidus, H. procerus.* 10–12, *Loxops parva, L. virens, L. coccinea.* 13, *Drepanidis pacifica.* 14, *Vestiaria coccinea.* 15, *Himatione sanguinea.* 16, *Palmeria dolei.* 17, *Ciridops anna.*

step to a diet of nothing but insects. *Hemignathus wilsoni* uses its mandible, which is slightly shorter than the upper half of its bill, to probe into crevices in bark for insects, and *Pseudonestor xanthophrys* uses its heavier bill to rip open twigs and branches in search of insects. Species of the genus *Psittacirostra* too, have heavy, powerful beaks, which some use for cracking open seeds, nuts or beans. The light bill of the recently extinct *Ciridops* was used for eating the soft flesh of the fruits of the Hawaiian palm *Pritchardia*.

Living as they do on fruits, seeds, nectar and insects, it is not surprising that none of the drepanidids shows the island-fauna characteristic of loss of flight. However, both on Hawaii and on Laysan to the west, some genera of the Rallidae (rails) have become flightless (a common occurrence in this particular family of birds). The phenomenon of flightlessness is also common in Hawaiian insects: of the endemic species of carabid beetle, 184 are flightless and only 20 fully winged. The Neuroptera or lacewings are another example—their wings, usually large and translucent, are reduced in size in some species, while in other species they have become thickened and spiny.

To summarize, islands provide a unique opportunity to study evolution, for their small, impoverished faunas and floras are the ideal situation for rapid evolutionary modification and adaptive radiation. At the same time, island life is unusually hazardous, so that there is a complex interaction between the processes of immigration, colonization and extinction; quantitative analysis of this has recently commenced and is proving extremely valuable in providing insights into the history and structure of ecosystems, on the continents as well as on islands.

References

1 RIDLEY H.N. (1930) *The Dispersal of Plants throughout the World.* Reeve & Co., Ashford.
2 PORTER D.M. (1976) Geography and dispersal of Galápagos Islands vascular plants. *Nature, Lond.* **264**, 745–746.
3 WHITEHEAD D.R. & JONES C.E. (1969) Small islands and the equilibrium theory of insular biogeography. *Evolution* **23**, 171–179.
4 JOHNSON M.P., MASON L.G. & RAVEN P.H. (1968) Ecological parameters and plant species diversity. *Am. Nat.* **102**, 297–306.
5 VAN BALGOOY M.M.J. (1971) Plant-geography of the Pacific as based on a census of phanerogam genera. *Blumea Suppl.* **6**, 1–222.
6 MAYR E. (1933) Die Vogelwelt Polynesiens. *Mit. zool. Mus. Berlin* **19**, 306–323.
7 MACARTHUR R.H. & WILSON E.O. (1963) An equilibrium theory of insular biogeography. *Evolution* **17**, 373–387.
8 MACARTHUR R.H., DIAMOND J.M. & KARR J. (1972) Density compensation in island faunas. *Ecology* **53**, 330–342.
9 LACK D. (1969) Subspecies and sympatry in Darwin's finches. *Evolution* **23**, 252–263.
10 CROWELL K.L. (1973) Experimental zoogeography: introductions of mice to small islands. *Am. Nat.* **107**, 535–558.
11 SIMBERLOFF D.S. (1978) Using island biogeographic distributions to determine if colonization is stochastic. *Am. Nat.* **112**, 713–726.
12 MACARTHUR R.H. & WILSON E.O. (1967) *The Theory of Island Biogeography.* Princeton University Press, Princeton.
13 SNOW B.K. & SNOW D.W. (1971) The feeding ecology of tanagers and honey-creepers in Trinidad. *Auk* **88**, 291–322.
14 WILLIAMS E.E. (1969) The ecology of colonization as seen in the zoogeography of anoline lizards on small islands. *Q. Rev. Biol.* **44**, 345–389.
15 SIMBERLOFF D.S. & WILSON E.O. (1970) Experimental zoogeography of islands; a two-year record of colonization. *Ecology* **51**, 934–937.
16 WILCOX B.A. (1978) Supersaturated island faunas: a species-age relationship for lizards on post-Pleistocene land-bridge islands. *Science* **199**, 996–998.
17 FRYER G. & ILES T.D. (1972) *The Cichlid Fishes of the Great Lakes of Africa: their Biology and Evolution.* Oliver & Boyd, Edinburgh.
18 CARLQUIST S. (1965) *Island Life.* Natural History Press, New York.
19 STONE B.S. (1967) A review of the endemic genera of Hawaiian plants. *Bot. Rev.* **33**, 216–259.
20 ZIMMERMAN E.C. (1948) *The Insects of Hawaii: I. Introduction.* University of Hawaii Press, Honolulu.
21 ROBERTSON F.W. (1970) Evolutionary divergence in Hawaiian *Drosophila. Sci. Prog., Oxf.* **58**, 525–538.
22 CARSON H.L., HARDY D.E., SPIETH H.T. & STONE W.S. (1970) The evolutionary biology of the Hawaiian Drosophilidae. In: Hecht M.K. and Steere W.C. (eds), *Essays in Evolution and Genetics in Honour of Theodosius Dobzhansky,* pp. 437–543. North-Holland Publishing Co., Amsterdam.

23 CARLQUIST S. (1970) *Hawaii, a Natural History*. Natural History Press, New York.
24 RAIKOW R.J. (1976) The origin and evolution of the Hawaiian honey-creepers (Drepanididae). *Living Bird* **15**, 95–117.

CHAPTER 6

THE DISTANT PAST

As explained in Chapter 2, one way of grouping the terrestrial biological communities of the world is to place each of them in one of eight biomes. Each of these is distinguished from the others by its characteristic climate. A particular biome, such as desert, may therefore exist in many different parts of the world. In each desert live animals and plants of broadly similar appearance and way of life, but these may belong to quite different groups from those found in a similar desert in another part of the world. A map showing the distribution of the biomes therefore tells us nothing about the patterns of distribution of taxonomic groups of animals or about the way in which different groups replace one another.

An alternative approach to classifying the patterns of distribution is to subdivide the world's surfaces into regions which appear to differ from one another in the dominant types of plant or animal to be found there. Although very few groups have precisely the same pattern of geographical distribution, there are some zones which mark the limits of distribution of many groups. This is because these zones are barrier regions, where conditions are so inhospitable to most organisms that few of them can live there. For terrestrial animals, any stretch of sea or ocean proves to be a barrier of this kind—except for flying animals whose distribution is for this reason obviously wider than that of solely terrestrial forms. Extremes of temperature, such as exist in deserts or in high mountains, constitute similar (though less effective) barriers to the spread of plants and animals.

These three types of barrier—oceans, mountain chains and large deserts—therefore provide the major discontinuities in the patterns of the spread of organisms around the world. Oceans completely surround Australia. They also virtually isolate South America and North America from each other and completely separate them from other continents. Seas, and the extensive deserts of North Africa and the Middle East, effectively isolate Africa from Eurasia. India and south-east Asia are similarly isolated from the rest of Asia by the vast, high Tibetan Plateau, of which the Himalayas are the southern fringe, together with the Asian deserts which lie to the north.

Each of these great land areas, together with any nearby islands to which its fauna or flora has been able to spread, is therefore comparatively isolated. It is not surprising to find that the patterns of distribution of both the faunas (*faunal provinces* or *zoogeographical regions*) and the floras (*floral regions*) largely reflect this pattern of geographical barriers. The two schemes differ mainly in that the pattern of floral regions shows a closer relationship to the latitudinally determined pattern of climate (cf. Fig. 7.1, p. 162 and Fig. 7.6, p. 172). Thus the north temperate areas (North

America and Eurasia) are linked together into a single floral region, while the temperate southern extremities of South America and of Africa are recognized as separate floral regions.

Before the detailed composition of these faunal provinces and floral regions can be understood fully, it is first necessary to explain the ways in which today's patterns of geography, climate and distribution of life came into existence. From what has been discussed in earlier chapters, it is clear that the differences between the faunas and floras of different areas might be due to a number of factors. Firstly, any new group of organisms will appear first in one particular area. If it competes with another, previously established group in that area, the expansion in the range of distribution of the new group may be accompanied by contraction in that of the old. However, once it has spread to the limits of its province or region, whether or not it is able to spread into the next will depend initially on whether it is able to surmount the geographical ocean or mountain barrier, or to adapt to the different climatic conditions to be found there. (Though, even if it is able to cross to the next province or region, it may be unable to establish itself because of the presence there of another group which is better adapted to that particular environment.) Of course, changes in the climate or geographical pattern could lead to changes in the patterns of distribution of life. For example, gradual climatic changes, affecting the whole world, could cause the gradual northward or southward migrations of floras and faunas, because these extended into newly favourable areas and died out in areas where the climate was no longer hospitable. Similarly, the possibilities of migration between different areas could change if vital links between them became broken by the appearance of new barriers, or if new links appeared.

Until recently, it seemed as though the geographical ranges of different animals and plants could be explained using only three basic principles—evolution, climatic change and land bridges. Such a belief was supported by evidence from the most recent (and therefore best documented) past. The Pleistocene changes in the ranges of the plants and animals of North America and Eurasia could be straightforwardly explained as the results of expansions and contractions of the ice-sheets which covered the northern parts of the two continents during much of this period. These recent changes, which are described in the next chapter, presumably resulted from more general changes in the Earth's climate. In North America, studies had been made of the thick sediments, eroded from the Rocky Mountains, that had been deposited over the Mid-Western part of the country. Extending back for the whole of the Cenozoic Era, which (as can be seen from the geological time scale, Fig. 6.1) lasted 65 million years, these too showed that the climate of the North American continent had gradually become colder during that time. The effects of this cooling had included the Bering area between Siberia and Alaska which, as a result, had gradually become inaccessible as a migration route to all but the most hardy animals and plants.

Though it was clear that such geological events as the rising of mountain chains must inevitably have affected the climate of surrounding

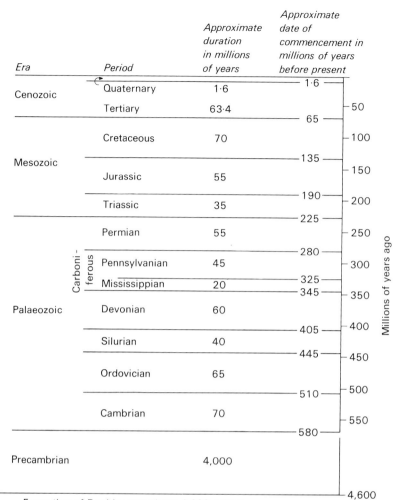

Era	Period		Approximate duration in millions of years	Approximate date of commencement in millions of years before present
Cenozoic	Quaternary		1·6	1·6
	Tertiary		63·4	65
Mesozoic	Cretaceous		70	135
	Jurassic		55	190
	Triassic		35	225
Palaeozoic	Permian		55	280
	Carboniferous	Pennsylvanian	45	325
		Mississippian	20	345
	Devonian		60	405
	Silurian		40	445
	Ordovician		65	510
	Cambrian		70	580
Precambrian			4,000	

Formation of Earth's crust about 4,600 million years ago

Durations of the Epochs of the Cenozoic Era
Pleistocene Epoch   1·6 – 0   million years ago
Pliocene Epoch   5·0 – 1·6   ″   ″   ″
Miocene Epoch   22·5 – 5·0   ″   ″   ″
Oligocene Epoch   37·0 – 22·5   ″   ″   ″
Eocene Epoch   53·5 – 37·0   ″   ″   ″
Paleocene Epoch   65·0 – 53·5   ″   ″   ″

Figure 6.1. Geological time scale.

areas, there seemed until recently no reason to search for new principles to explain the distribution of animals, plants or climates during the whole of the Cenozoic, and the same could also be said for much of the preceding Mesozoic Era. But studies of the late Palaeozoic Era (about 225–300 million years ago) provided evidence of a very different world.

Gondwanaland and Laurasia One of the first clues to this was the discovery that the flora that had covered the southern continents during the Permian was rather different from that found in the northern continents. One of the groups common to all the floras was the seed-ferns, which, as their name implies, were very like living ferns but bore large seeds instead of small spores. The Permian southern flora was dominated by seed-ferns belonging to the genera *Glossopteris* and *Gangamopteris*—it is usually called the *Glossopteris* flora. Its distribution extended over South America, South and Central Africa, Australia, Antarctica and India. All these areas are collectively known as *Gondwanaland*; North America, Greenland and Eurasia, from which the *Glossopteris* flora was absent, are

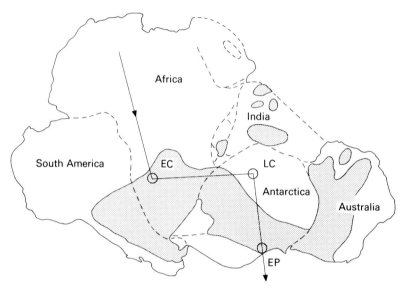

Figure 6.2. Glaciers are known to have occurred within the shaded areas of Gondwanaland, and probably also covered some of the intervening regions. But these areas were not all glaciated at the same time, because the centre of glaciation shifted as Gondwanaland moved across the South Pole. The position of the South Pole in the Early Carboniferous (EC), Late Carboniferous (LC) and Early Permian (EP) is shown by small circles.

known as *Laurasia*. The presence of this flora in India was unexpected, because on the basis of present-day geography one might expect its flora to be like that of Asia and unlike that of the southern continents. India was also found to be peculiar in another way. Shortly before the appearance of the *Glossopteris* flora, all the southern continents had been affected by a giant glaciation. The evidence for this lies in the thick drift deposits of rock-rubble or *till* (see p. 184) that these glaciers had carried, and that had been left behind as they melted. Surprisingly, the southern glaciation had affected not only Australia, South America, and South Africa, but also India (Fig. 6.2).

The idea of continental drift   The unexpected distributions of Permian and Carboniferous floras and glaciers could most simply be explained if the continents had at that time been joined together in a pattern different from that seen today, and had also lain farther south than they do now (Fig. 6.2). They would then have had to drift apart and northward to reach their present positions. Several scientists in the early years of the 20th century had noticed the great similarity between the outlines of the continents on either side of the Atlantic, and had suggested that they had once been joined and later moved apart. In 1910 the American geologist F. B. Taylor, for example, suggested that movements of this kind might have been responsible for the formation of the major mountain ranges of the world. Up to that time, however, the possibility of continental movement was put forward as an explanation of isolated phenomena of geology, without any real attempt to analyse all the different results such movements might have had, or to find evidence that they *had* happened. Such analyses and evidence were first provided by the German scientist Alfred Wegener. He, too, had been impressed by the similar shapes of the coastlines on either side of the Atlantic, but in the autumn of 1911 he accidentally chanced upon a report containing details of palaeontological evidence for an ancient land connection between Brazil and Africa. Further research into the literature of palaeontology and geology soon provided a wealth of additional evidence. For example, Wegener found that, if the edges of the continental shelves on either side of the Atlantic were fitted together, many geological features that had previously ended abruptly at the edge of one continent were now continuous with a similar feature on the adjacent continent. At the same time, his reconstruction solved the problems of the extent of the great southern glaciation and of the distribution of the *Glossopteris* flora.

A geological controversy   Wegener's theory, which was first published in 1915, demanded radical changes in the beliefs of scientists in many fields of geology and related sciences. For this reason alone, it would probably have been slow to find acceptance even if it had come from a worker with a long history of research and publication in geology. Wegener, however, was primarily a meteorologist and astronomer, whose earlier published work had been on the thermodynamics of the atmosphere. Geologists were, perhaps naturally, even less ready to change the whole basis of their approach to the structure of the Earth at the suggestion of such an outsider. Many scientists 'solved' the problem to their own satisfaction by suggesting solutions that left the theories in their own branch of science unchanged at the expense of radical changes in other sciences. For example, many biologists suggested that the different parts of Gondwanaland had been connected by land bridges that had allowed animals and plants to migrate between them. Geologists at that time did not know enough about the ocean beds to prove that such land bridges were impossible. Some geologists even suggested that the glaciers had never existed, the supposed glacial tills being the result of mud flows of

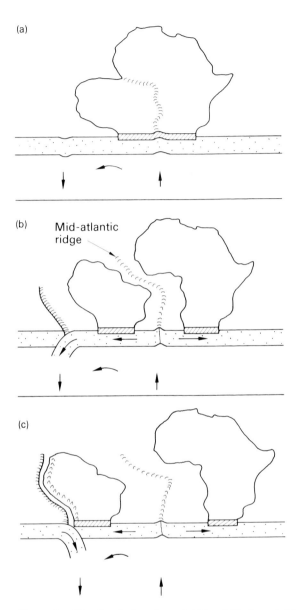

(a)

(b) Mid-atlantic ridge

(c)

Figure 6.4. How South America and Africa drifted apart. (a) The two continents were originally part of a single supercontinent. A convection cell appeared in the deeper layers of the earth, an upward continent appearing under the layers of the supercontinent and a downward current from the west. (b) The supercontinent splits above the ascending current. New crustal material (flooring the new South Atlantic Ocean) appears on either side of this split line, which now forms the mid-Atlantic ridge. At the same time, an ocean trench forms above the descending current and old crustal material disappears into this. (c) South America has moved westward until it is adjacent to the oceanic trench. The crustal material consumed by the trench is now derived from the west; its movement below western South America causes earthquakes, and the raising of this region forms the Andes.

while the trenches indicate where the corresponding downward currents return cooler material to the depths of the Earth.

Plate tectonics   Where spreading ridges lie within the oceans, their activity will cause continents to move apart, and ultimately may cause them to collide with one another, the collision raising mountains such as the Himalayas and Urals. A ridge may also gradually elongate and extend under a continent; its activity will then cause the gradual rifting apart of those regions of the continent that lie on either side of the spreading ridge (Fig. 6.4). As these move apart, they become separated by a new, widening ocean, the floor of which is similarly moving to one side or the other, away from the spreading ridge. The moving units at the surface of the Earth are therefore areas which may contain continental masses, or which may consist only of ocean-floor. These units are known as 'plates', and Earth scientists today refer to 'plate tectonics' rather than to 'continental drift' (Fig. 6.5).

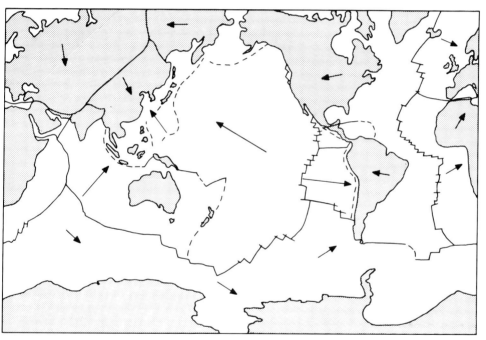

Figure 6.5. The major plates today. Single lines within the oceans show the positions of spreading ridges, dotted lines show the positions of trenches. Lines within the continents show the divisions between the Eurasian, African, Indian, China and North American plates. Arrows show the directions and proportionate speeds of movement of the plates. The Antarctic plate is moving clockwise.

Changing patterns of continents   The true edges of the continents are marked, not by their coastlines, but by the edge of the continental shelf. Between the continental shelves, the deep oceans separate the continental plates. Sometimes the whole of these plates have been above

(a) Late Carboniferous – Early Permian

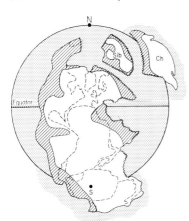

(b) Late Permian – Triassic

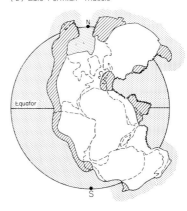

(c) Mid – Jurassic

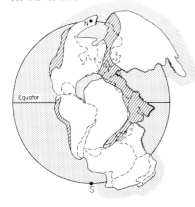

(d) Early Cretaceous

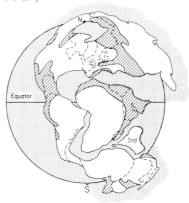

(e) Late Cretaceous

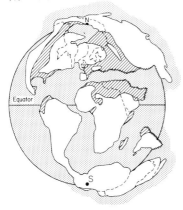

(f) Early Cenozoic

The Distant Past

sea-level. At other times shallow 'epicontinental' seas have covered the edges of the continent to form the shelf seas (such as the North Sea today) or penetrated further inland (like Hudson's Bay today). Though the extent of these shallow seas varied, they must have formed a barrier to the spread of terrestrial organisms, and they are shown in Figure 6.6. They were particularly extensive in the Jurassic and Cretaceous.

The stretch of time occupied by the Silurian and Devonian Periods is the earliest for which there is good evidence of the overall geography of the world. Gondwanaland was by then already a single unit, and surrounded the South Pole. Europe and North America had recently united (the impact raising the Appalachian and Caledonian mountain chains) and lay near the Equator. Siberia and China were still separate continents.

By the Late Carboniferous (Fig. 6.6a), Gondwanaland had united with the Euramerican continent to form a supercontinent stretching from Alaska in the north to Australia in the south. Siberia collided with this in the Middle Permian, the impact raising the Ural Mountains, while China collided a little later. By the Late Permian, all the continents had thus united to form a single supercontinent, which is often called Pangaea (Fig. 6.6b).

However, it was not long before the Pangaea land mass started to become divided. This took place in two ways. Firstly, Gondwanaland started to drift away from North America, and then started to break up. Secondly, shallow epicontinental seas penetrated far across both North America and Asia. Both these processes started in the Jurassic and continued throughout the Cretaceous Period (Fig. 6.6c, d). In the Late Cretaceous (Fig. 6.6e) Europe was still separated from Asia by the Obik Sea, and the Mid-Continental Seaway completely bisected North America into eastern and western land areas. The western part was connected to Asia via Alaska and Siberia to form a single 'Asiamerican' land mass, and the eastern portion was connected to Europe via Greenland to form a 'Euramerican' land mass. At the same time, South America finally became separated from Africa, but it may have remained connected to Antarctica (and thence also to Australia) until the end of the Cretaceous. India probably separated from the rest of Gondwanaland in the Early Cretaceous.

It was not until the Early Cenozoic that the geography of the world became basically similar to that we see today (Fig. 6.6f). In the Middle Eocene, about 45 million years ago, Australia separated from Antarctica, and India became united with Asia. At the same time, Europe became

Figure 6.6. Six stages in the changing geography of the world. Lambert equal-area projection; areas lying within the circle lie on the front hemisphere of this view of the globe, and any areas which are outside the circle lie on the back hemisphere. Dotted lines indicate the coast-lines of the modern continents. The position of the islands of south-east Asia is uncertain, and this area has been omitted. Zig-zag lines indicate continental edges which later collided with one another. Hatched areas indicate epicontinental seas, dark tint indicates oceans. Ant., Antarctica; Aus., Australia; Ch., China; N. and S., North and South Poles respectively; Sib., Siberia.

separate from Greenland, and the drying of the Obik Sea finally made Europe continuous with Asia. Though the continents of Africa and Eurasia had for long been close together, shallow seas separated their land areas from one another until the Miocene. The final link, between South America and North America, did not form until the Late Pliocene.

Effect on climate   The movements of the continents appear to have been quite slow—only about 5 to 10 cm a year. These movements must have affected life in several ways, even though the changes must have been incredibly gradual, and noticeable only over a period of millions of years. The most obvious change would have resulted directly from the movement of the supercontinents relative to the poles of the Earth, and relative to the Equator. As they moved, so the different areas of land would eventually have come to lie in cold polar regions, in the hot, wet equatorial regions, in the dry subtropical regions, or in the cool, damp temperate regions.[3,4] Drift also affected the climates of the continents in two less direct ways. Before the break-up, much of the area of the supercontinents lay far from the sea and must have had fairly stable climates. More variable, wetter weather must have affected greater areas when the seas gradually spread between the drifting continents as they separated. The northward movement of North America and Eurasia may even be a major cause of the glacial eras of the Late Cenozoic.[5]

The pattern of ocean spreading ridges, as well as the resulting splitting and movement of the continents themselves, will also have affected their climates because of their effects on the patterns of circulation of water in the oceans. For example, the cold Humboldt Current up the western side of southern South America, the cold Benguela Current up the western side of southern Africa, the warm clockwise Gulf Stream of the North Atlantic, and the southward movement of cold deep water from the Arctic Ocean into the North Atlantic, all result from the present pattern of continents and all affect the climates of the neighbouring continents. The different continental patterns of the past would therefore have resulted in different patterns of ocean circulation, and different climates.[6] It has been suggested that these changes in circulation pattern may also have contributed to the initiation of the Late Cenozoic glacial epochs (see p. 206).

It has recently been suggested that plate tectonic activity may also have a direct effect on continental climates by controlling the extent of the epicontinental seas.[7] There appears to be a correlation between the total length of the system of oceanic spreading ridges and the extent of the transgression of seas over the continents. Because the ridges are formed of high submarine mountain chains, an increase in their length will decrease the capacity of the ocean basins and cause an overspill of water onto the continents as epicontinental seas.

Furthermore, the distribution of climate within the continental masses must also have been affected by the appearance of new mountain ranges as a result of continental drift. These would have had particularly great effects on the climate of the continents if they arose across the paths of the prevailing moisture-bearing winds, since areas in the lee of the mountains would then become desert. These can be seen today in the Andes, to the east of the mountain chain in southern Argentina, and to the west along the coast from northern Argentina to Peru; the winds in these two regions blow in opposite directions. A huge area of desert, including the arid wastes of the Gobi Desert of outer Mongolia, has also formed in central Asia, far from seas from which winds could gain moisture.

Early land life in the moving continents   Over the last few years, understanding of the movements of the continents, and of the timing of the different episodes of continental fragmentation or union, has become fairly detailed. It is now possible to show that the distribution of fossil organisms correlates very well with the varying patterns of land, and to understand how the present-day patterns of distribution of land plants and of terrestrial vertebrates came into existence.

Vascular plants first appeared in the Late Silurian, and woody tree-like plants up to 25 m high had evolved by the Late Devonian. Though our information on this early period is still limited, as far as one can tell there were no separate floral regions in the Devonian. This is surprising, since there were several continental masses at that time, and we can only surmise that the spores of these early land plants were light enough to be distributed by the wind even over great distances, like those of ferns today (see p. 134). Until recently, it was thought that there was similarly only a single flora in the Early Carboniferous. Known as the *Lepidodendropsis* flora, this was composed of lycopsids (related to the tiny living club-moss *Lycopodium*), seed ferns and sphenopsids (related to the living horse-tail *Equisetum*). This flora is known from Euramerica and from several parts of Gonwanaland,[8] but it has now become clear that the Early Carboniferous flora of Siberia already had some distinctive features.[9]

During the Late Carboniferous, the isolation of the different continents, together with their differing climates, started to lead to the appearance of several distinct floras. The Euramerican continent, for example, then lay across the Equator (Fig. 6.6a), and large parts of the continent were covered by swampy, tropical rain forest—an environment rather like that of the Amazon rain forest of today. The absence of dormant buds and of annual growth rings in the fossil remains of this vegetation indicates that it grew in an unvarying, seasonless climate. The flora was dominated by great trees belonging to several quite distinct groups (Fig. 6.7). *Lepidodendron*, 40 m tall, and *Sigillaria* 30 m tall, were enormous types of lycopod. Equally tall *Cordaites* was a member of the group from which the conifer trees evolved, and the sphenopsid *Calamites* was up to 15 m high. Tree-ferns such as *Psaronius* grew up to $7\frac{1}{2}$ m high, and seed-ferns such as *Neuropteris* were among the most common smaller plants living around the trunks of all these great trees. In the eastern United States and in parts of Britain and central Europe, the land covered by this swamp forest was gradually sinking. As it sank, the basins that formed became filled with the accumulated remains of these ancient trees. Compressed by

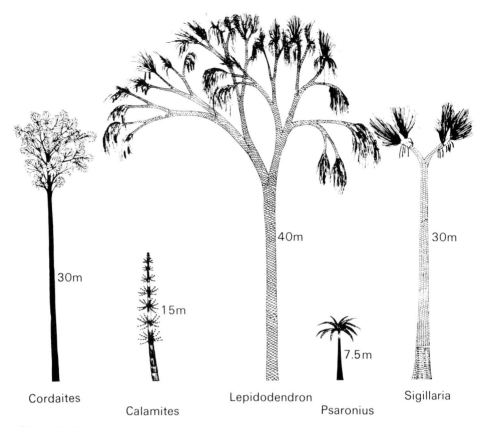

Cordaites

Calamites

Lepidodendron

Psaronius

Sigillaria

Figure 6.7. Coal forest trees.

the overlying sediment, dried, and hardened, the plant remains have become the coal deposits of these regions.

By the Late Carboniferous and Early Permian, five distinct floras had appeared (Fig. 6.6a).[8,9] These floras were not completely different from one another: some genera or families of plant are found in more than one floral region, or in all of them. The climate of Euramerica became drier, perhaps because the fusion of Gondwanaland and Euramerica had displaced the moisture-giving ocean that had previously lain between them. The rich flora of the moist coal-swamps disappeared, and lycopod trees (such as *Sigillaria* and *Lepidodendron*) were less common. Instead, the commonest trees in this region were early types of true conifer. This *Euramerican flora* also included early fern-like plants, seed-ferns and horsetails.

A separate *North American flora* can be recognized in the western parts of what is now the United States, and this can even be subdivided into three geographic areas characterized respectively by the seed-ferns *Gigantopteris americana*, *Glenopteris*, and *Supaia*. Though it was long thought that this North American flora was similar to the Cathaysian flora of eastern Asia, this is no longer accepted by all modern workers.

Because the regions now known as Siberia and China (including south-east Asia) were still separate continents at this time, they contained different floras. The *Angara flora* of Siberia was characterized by *Cordaites*-like plants and the seed-fern *Angaropteridium*, and conifers were less common. In China and south-east Asia there was a *Cathaysian* flora dominated by ferns and seed-ferns, and characterized by the sphenopsid *Lobatannularia*; conifers and calamites were rare in this flora.

As already mentioned, the great glaciation of the different parts of Gondwanaland in the Carboniferous and Early Permian confirms the fact that the supercontinent lay around the South Pole at that time. But, as Gondwanaland moved across the South Pole, the glaciated area moved also (Fig. 6.2). In the Late Carboniferous, the characteristic *Glossopteris flora* developed within the cool–temperate parts of Gondwanaland. This is the most distinctive of all these floras, the woody shrubs that included *Glossopteris* and its relatives being found only in that region. *Calamites* trees were absent from the *Glossopteris* flora, and lycopods, ferns, and seed-ferns were less important there than in the north. The reasons for the contrast are uncertain, but it may have resulted from the Early Carboniferous situation, in which Gondwanaland was more isolated than the other continents, while parts of it experienced a harsh glacial age in the Late Carboniferous. This history may have caused the evolution, from the older Devonian–Early Carboniferous flora, of unique cold-adapted plants which were not well-suited to dispersal northwards into warmer lands. (It is their southward penetration, to within $5°$ of the then South Pole, that is surprising for, even though the polar ice-caps had disappeared, this region must have had an extremely short period of daylight for part of the year. The very marked seasonal growth rings of plants from these regions are therefore not surprising, though the size of these is unexpectedly great from so high a latitude.) A few instances are known in which northern genera have been found associated with the *Glossopteris* flora[10]: as might be expected, these examples are all from warmer, more peripheral parts of Gondwanaland, and belong to spore-producing plants which could more readily have dispersed across an ocean barrier.[8]

The patterns of distribution of the earliest land vertebrates also correlate well with these patterns of continents.[11] The earliest amphibians are known from Euramerica and, until the Middle Permian, terrestrial amphibians and reptiles are almost unknown outside that single continent. The few exceptions, such as the little reptile *Mesosaurus* found in Brazil and southern Africa, are nearly all aquatic forms which could have crossed the intervening sea barriers. There is good geological evidence that Asia did not fuse with Euramerica until the Middle Permian. The geological evidence of the date of the union of Gondwanaland with the northern continents is less certain, but the almost total lack of Gondwanaland land vertebrates until the Late Permian suggests that, until then, there was some barrier to the dispersal of land vertebrates into Gondwanaland; it is impossible to know whether the barrier was a shallow sea or a combination of mountains and deserts with their rigorous climates.

One world—for a while   We live today in a world in which there are polar ice-caps, so that there is a very great difference between the climate of the Equator and that of the Poles, and a correspondingly steep gradient of climatic change between these regions. But such glacial periods seem to have been the exception, rather than the norm, in Earth's history. The polar glaciation of the Late Carboniferous and Early Permian had disappeared by the Late Permian, and warm climates seem to have extended into quite high latitudes. But the geography of Pangaea showed clear traces of its earlier history. The Ural Mountains between Europe and Asia, and the mountain ranges of what is now eastern North America, must then have been lofty reminders of the union of Euramerica, Asia and Gondwanaland. Because of the disappearance of the oceans that had previously lain between these continents, and the retreat of the shallow sea that had previously covered large areas of the continents (Fig. 6.6a), vast regions now lay far from any source of moist, rain-bearing winds. Continental climates, therefore, became much drier in the Late Permian and Early Triassic. This climatic change is one of the probable causes of the great floral change that commenced in the Middle Permian. Old types of tree, such as those belonging to the lycopods and sphenopsids, and *Cordaites*, disappeared. Their places were taken by the radiation of existing types of the tree, such as caytonias and ginkgos, or by new groups such as cycads and bennettitaleans. A new type of fern, the osmundas, also appeared. The floral change was complete by the Late Triassic.

The pattern of spread of these new groups seems to have been conditioned by two factors. Firstly, the polar and equatorial regions must have had different climates (even if far less different than do those of today). Secondly, the floras of the different areas were not identical, for they contained the survivors of the old Early Permian floral regions. The southern, Gondwanaland region seems to have remained the most distinct, though in the Early Triassic *Glossopteris* itself was replaced by the seed-fern *Dicroidium*. This was similarly restricted to Gondwanaland, and the region continued to be florally distinct into the Early Jurassic.[12] In general, floras in the Jurassic and Early Cretaceous seem to have gradually become more similar to one another, approaching the modern pattern in which there are gradual latitudinal changes governed by climate, and which manifest themselves as changing patterns in the dominance of different groups as one moves from lower latitudes to higher latitudes. For example, a separate Siberian floral province, adapted to a cooler climate, can be distinguished in the northern part of Asia and North America. The southern boundary of this floral province moved northwards between the Late Jurassic and Early Cretaceous. This seems to have been caused by a climatic change, the southern part of Asia becoming increasingly hot and arid. Unlike today's pattern, however, the Mesozoic floras extended to high (about 70°) northern and southern latitudes, to areas which, although clearly warm, must have had seasonal periods of very brief daylight.[9]

These northern floras show clear evidence that the world's climate began to cool in the Middle Cretaceous. For example, a series of floras from about 70°N in Alaska, ranging through about 30 million years of the

Middle Cretaceous, shows that both the climate and the flora changed considerably.[13] The earliest of these floras contains the remains of a forest dominated by ferns and by gymnosperms such as cycads, ginkgos and conifers. The nearest living relatives of this flora are found in forests at moderate heights in warm–temperate areas at about 25–30°N—for example, in south-east Asia. By the time of the last of the Middle Cretaceous Alaskan floras, the flora had changed in two ways. Firstly, the angiosperms had by this time diversified to such an extent that they dominated the flora. Second, this flora contains the remains of forest similar to that found today at a latitude of 35–45°N in the region of North China and Korea—much farther north than the living relatives of the earlier flora. The differences between these successive fossil floras therefore suggest that the climate of northern Alaska was already becoming cooler in the Middle Cretaceous. Further south, however, floras from Sakhalin, at 45°N, show that the diversity of the gymnosperms increased during the Late Cretaceous and that they were still dominant until there was a major floral change at the end of the Cretaceous.[14]

To outline now the biogeographic history of the vertebrate animals of Pangaea, one must return to the Permian and Triassic, soon after that supercontinent formed. The early land vertebrates (amphibians and reptiles) appear to have been quite competent at dispersing through regions of differing climate, and Pangaea soon came to contain a fairly uniform fauna, with little sign of distinct faunal regions.[15] Nearly 60 families of Triassic land vertebrate have been described, and their distribution provides overwhelming evidence for the existence of a Pangaea world continent within which they would travel freely. The Triassic faunas of most of today's continents can be compared with one another (those of Antarctica and Australia are still too poorly known to be analysed in this way, but what has been found shows clearly that the same Triassic fauna was present in those two areas also). The comparison uses the index of faunal similarity, $100C/C_1$, in which C is the number of families common to the two continents being compared, and C_1 is the number of families in whichever has the smaller fauna. Thus, for example, 14 of the 16 families found in the Triassic of North America are also known in Europe, and the coefficient for this comparison is therefore $100 \times 14/16 = 87 \cdot 5$ per cent. As can be seen in Figure 6·8, these faunas are remarkably similar to one another—in fact, no less similar than are the mammal faunas of New York State and Oregon today.

Great changes took place in the world-wide fauna during the Triassic.[16] The bulk of the Permian faunas had been made up of mammal-like reptiles and other older types of reptile. These disappeared during the Early and Middle Triassic, and were at first replaced by a radiation of the early archosaurian reptiles. These in their turn were soon replaced (in the Late Triassic) by their own descendants, the dinosaurs, which came to dominate the world throughout the Jurassic and Cretaceous. Though comparatively little is known about Jurassic dinosaurs, it is enough to show that they were able to spread throughout the world. Their route between North America and Asia must have been via Alaska and Siberia,

	Europe (4)	Asia (18·5)	South America (19)	Africa (42·5)	India (16)
North America (16)	87·5%	44%	56%	75%	59%
Europe		81%	73%	60%	82·5%
Asia			51%	89%	41%
South America				74%	56%
Africa					75%

Figure 6.8. Coefficients of faunal similarity at family level between the Triassic faunas of today's continents. The number shown in parentheses after each continent shows the number of terrestrial Triassic families found in that continent; where the presence of a family is not yet fully confirmed, a score of 0·5 has been added.

which may still have had quite mild climates. That the dinosaurs were also able to reach Gondwanaland is shown by the similarities between the Jurassic dinosaur faunas of North America and of East Africa. In these two areas are found not only the same families of dinosaur but also, in some cases, the same genera—for example, the sauropod dinosaurs *Brachiosaurus, Bothriospondylus* and *Barosaurus,* and the ornithopod *Dryosaurus.* Although the position of the land connection between Gondwanaland and the north is unknown, it seems likely that it was via South America.[17]

Neither the dominant groups of animals or plants of the Early Cretaceous, nor the interconnections of the world's land areas at that time, were very different from those of the Triassic. Dramatic changes in all of these were evident by the Late Cretaceous, and the transition to the very different world of today will be followed in the next chapter.

References

1   WEGENER A. (1929) *The Origin of Continents and Oceans,* 4th edn. (1966 English translation). Methuen, London.
2   HALLAM A. (1973) *A Revolution in the Earth Sciences.* Clarendon Press, Oxford.
3   ROBINSON P.L. (1973) Palaeoclimatology and continental drift. In: Tarling D.H. and Runcorn S.K. (eds.), *Implications of Continental Drift to the Earth Sciences,* vol. I, pp. 451–476. Academic Press, London & New York.
4   FRAKES L.A. & KEMP E.M. (1973) Palaeogene continental positions and evolution of climate. *Ibid* I, 549–558.
5   DONN W.L. & SHAW D.M. (1977) Model of climate evolution based on continental drift and polar wandering. *Bull. geol. Soc. America* 88, 390–396.
6   BERGGREN W.A. & HOLLISTER C.D. (1977) Plate tectonics and paleocirculation—commotion in the ocean. *Tectonophysics* 38, 11–48.

7   HALLAM A. (1977) Secular changes in marine inundation of USSR and North America through the Phanerozoic. *Nature, Lond.* **269**, 769–772.

8   PAL A.K. & CHALONER W.G. (1979) A Lower Carboniferous *Lepidodendropsis* flora in Cashmere. *Nature, Lond.* **281**, 295–297.

9   CHALONER W.G. & LACEY W.S. (1973) The distribution of Late Palaeozoic floras. *Spec. Pap. Palaeontology* **12**, 271–289.

10 LACEY W.S. (1975) Some problems of 'mixed' floras in the Permian of Gondwanaland. In: Campbell K.S.W. (ed.), *Gondwana Geology*, pp. 125–134. Australian National University Press, Canberra.

11 Cox C.B. (1974) Vertebrate palaeodistributional patterns and continental drift. *J. Biogeog.* **1**, 75–94.

12 BARNARD P.D.W. (1973) Mesozoic floras. *Spec. Pap. Palaeontology* **12**, 175–187.

13 SMILEY C.J. (1966) Cretaceous floras from Kuk River area, Alaska: stratigraphic and climatic interpretations. *Bull. geol. Soc. America* **77**, 1–14.

14 KRASSILOV V.A. (1978) Late Cretaceous gymnosperms from Sakhalin and the terminal Cretaceous event. *Palaeontology* **21**, 893–905.

15 Cox C.B. (1973) Triassic tetrapods. In: Hallam A. (ed.), *Atlas of Palaeobiogeography*, pp. 213–223. Elsevier, Amsterdam.

16 Cox C.B. (1967) Changes in terrestrial vertebrate faunas during the Mesozoic. In: Harland W.B. *et al.* (eds), *The Fossil Record*, pp. 77–89. Geological Society, London.

17 GALTON P.M. (1977) The ornithopod dinosaur *Dryosaurus* and Laurasia–Gondwanaland connection in the Upper Jurassic. *Nature, Lond.* **268**, 230–232.

CHAPTER 7

THE SHAPING OF TODAY

In the 70 million years between the Early Cretaceous and the Eocene (one of the Epochs of the Cenozoic Era, see Figure 7.1) the world changed from a single land-mass dominated by gymnosperms and reptiles to a pattern of separating continents dominated by flowering plants and mammals. Because the rise of the flowering plants took place in the Late Cretaceous, before that of the mammals in the Paleocene, the effects of continental drift upon the distributions of these two groups were rather different.

Continental drift facilitated the development of separate, distinctive faunas and floras, not merely because of the physical separation of the new continents by ocean barriers, but in other ways also. The climates of land areas newly bordered by seas became milder and less variable. Where new mountain ranges lay across the path of the prevailing rain-bringing winds, new deserts grew in their lee. Finally, as the continents continued northward, their northern fringes reached such a high latitude that they became covered by permanent ice-sheets. This may have been the reason for the exaggeration and narrowing of the climatic zones; it may also have led in turn to the great Ice Ages of the Pleistocene, which wrought havoc upon the plant and animal life of the Northern Hemisphere. It is, perhaps, no mere coincidence that both the Permo-Carboniferous glaciation and the Pleistocene glaciations occurred at times when a considerable area of land lay near to one of the poles.

It is worth considering for a moment what patterns of distribution we might expect to find had the continents always had their present positions, so that the only changes would then have been the relatively minor climatic variations of the Northern Hemisphere Ice Ages, and changes in sea-level making or breaking the intercontinental Bering and Panama land bridges. At times when the climate was warmer than it is today, the spread of animals and plants across the Bering region between Siberia and Alaska would have been possible. Similarly, in the absence of the deserts of the Middle East, there would also have been a single tropical fauna and flora stretching from West Africa to south-east Asia. It would not be surprising, however, if the later development of these deserts, dividing the tropical region into African and Asian sections, had allowed distinctive features to appear in the faunas and floras of each. Finally, it might have been expected that the complete isolation of Australia and the almost complete isolation of South America would have led to the development of unique faunas and floras on these continents.

To some extent, it is indeed possible to distinguish such patterns of distribution in the world today but, as will be seen, there are other patterns which reveal older dispersal routes via continental links now long broken.

Historical biogeography and dispersal The different methods and capabilities of organisms for dispersal, together with the possibility of the extinction of any organism in a particular area, tempt the biogeographer to explain any patterns of discontinuous distribution in terms of these factors alone. The distribution of each organism is then apparently the result merely of its own biological characteristics of ecological limitation, competitive ability and dispersal. This may be true at lower taxonomic levels, where some individual species may not have existed for very long. Their present-day distributions are the result of these factors alone, and can therefore be explained simply in terms of biological characteristics that can be identified and studied experimentally in the world today.

But, in many other cases, this is not so. Higher taxonomic units (genera, families, orders) originated further back in time, so that their original dispersal will have been over different patterns of geography and climate. Even the distribution patterns of many species have been similarly influenced by the climatic changes of the Ice Ages of the last 2 million years. The need to invoke some such non-biological explanation can be realized only if the biogeographer compares the patterns of distribution of several quite different components of a biota and finds that, despite their differing ecologies or modes of dispersal, they share a common basic biogeographic pattern. For example, less attention might in the past have been paid to the particular dispersal abilities or ecology of the southern beech *Nothofagus* (see p. 176), had it been realized that its Southern Hemisphere pattern of distribution is merely a part of a biotic distribution found also in such diverse groups as earthworms, freshwater crustaceans and their parasites, molluscs, midges, galaxiid freshwater fishes, birds, and flowering plants other than *Nothofagus*.[1]

A good example of the more modern approach to such a problem is Donn Rosen's recent study of the Caribbean biota.[2] He analysed the patterns of distribution of many organisms (including bromeliads, cacti, gastropods, spiders, woodlice, crayfish, butterflies, sea-urchins, fish, frogs, toads, lizards, snakes, crocodiles, birds, opossums, bats, rodents and monkeys), and recognized four main underlying patterns (two terrestrial and two marine). Rosen then showed that each of these four generalized patterns can be explained as having resulted from dispersal of organisms over continuous areas of land or sea, at different stages of the evolution of Caribbean geography; their patterns of distribution had later become distorted and discontinuous as a result of subsequent geophysical events. It is clear that, to a modern biogeographer, the dispersal of an organism may have been caused by either, or both, of two independent processes: active dispersal, the organism having crossed barriers between the separate areas in which it is now found, and passive dispersal, the organism having merely remained on different land-masses, which themselves dispersed, causing barriers to arise within the once-continuous area of distribution of the organism (see also p. 178).

The patterns today   Any outline of the major patterns of distribution of life must be based upon the common, dominant groups, and it is not surprising to find that the zoogeographic regions are founded upon the distribution of mammals (though they were originally established on the distribution of birds), and the floral regions are based upon that of the angiosperms (flowering plants). The following account will attempt to integrate these biogeographic patterns with those of continental drift and climatic change. The biogeographic patterns of older, less dominant groups are complicated by the frequent presence of relict distributions. They are therefore less easy to interpret and contribute less to any general understanding of world biogeography, but valuable information has been published on lower land plants,[3] invertebrates in general,[4] insects,[5] fish and lower land vertebrates,[6] as well as a modern survey of bird biogeography.[7]

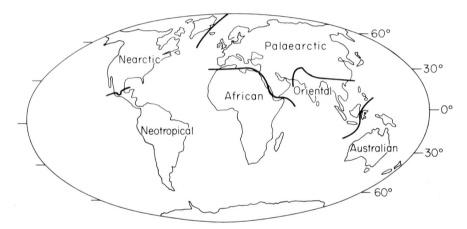

Figure 7.1. Zoogeographical regions of the world today, based on the distribution of mammals.

Although in general the biogeographic patterns of mammals and angiosperms are similar to one another, they differ in several details (compare Figs 7.1 and 7.6). The pattern of flowering plant distribution is less clearly determined by modern geography than is that of mammals. This is partly because, as has been seen (p. 118), flowering plants are much better at dispersal across ocean barriers than are the mammals, and partly because, unlike mammals, they radiated before the final break-up of Gondwanaland. Mammalian zoogeography therefore gives comparatively little hint of the occurrence of continental drift—which may explain why that theory was for so long rejected by such mammalian palaeontologists as George Simpson, and by the zoogeographer Philip Darlington, who has fully documented the present patterns of vertebrate distribution.[8]

The most obvious discrepancy between the two patterns lies in the relationship between south-east Asia and Australasia (Fig. 7.2). The series of islands between the mainlands of Asia and Australia contains a transition between the Asian flowering plants and placental mammals, and the

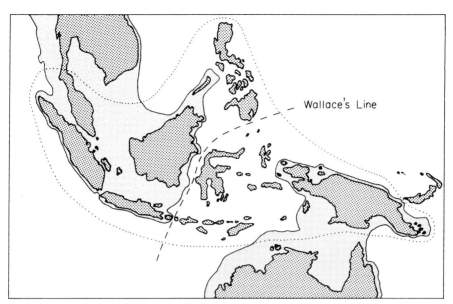

Figure 7.2. Map of south-east Asia and Australasia. The continental shelves are shown lightly shaded. The Malaysian floral province is shown outlined by a dotted line. Wallace's Line indicates the boundary between the Oriental and Australian faunal regions.

Australian flowering plants and marsupial mammals. The whole area is usually viewed by plant geographers as the Malaysian province of the Old World tropical floral region, which extends eastwards to include New Guinea. Zoogeographers, in contrast, recognize the line defined in the 19th century by Wallace, which separates Oriental and Australian faunas and which cuts across the middle of the Malaysian floral province. The reasons for these differing patterns will be discussed later (pp. 178–179), but they emphasize the extent to which any faunal or floral lines laid down on the varying and complex patterns of distribution of the world's living organisms are inevitably generalizations, and few groups will conform to them exactly.

The mammals supplant the reptiles   In the Cretaceous, dinosaurs were still the dominant land vertebrates and were still diversifying. The distribution of the new types of dinosaur that evolved during the Cretaceous mirrors the palaeogeographic maps very closely. Most of those that evolved during the Early Cretaceous (ostrich-dinosaurs, dome-headed dinosaurs, dromaeosaurs and primitive duck-billed dinosaurs) dispersed throughout the Northern Hemisphere (cf. Fig. 6.6d). Those types that did not evolve until near the end of the Late Cretaceous, however, showed a more restricted pattern of distribution: tyrannosaurs, protoceratopsids and advanced duck-billed dinosaurs are all found only in Asiamerica (cf. Fig. 6.6e). The ceratopsians, which evolved in the very latest Cretaceous in North America, did not even reach Asia, a fact which suggests that the sea had by then broken through the Bering Straits to separate Asia from North America.

There is little evidence for these Late Cretaceous groups in Gondwanaland (though this may be because of the relative poverty of the Cretaceous record from the Southern Hemisphere). In the Late Cretaceous, duck-billed dinosaurs and a possible ceratopsian are known from South America. There must, therefore, have been some dispersal route between North and South America during at least part of the Cretaceous, and this is supported by the Late Cretaceous dispersal of some mammals between the two continents (see below). Since only some representatives of the faunas of North and South America were able to disperse by this route, it must have been either a Panama-like narrow land-bridge or a sweepstakes route similar to the West Indies island chain of today.

Though the earliest mammals appeared in the Triassic, it was not until the Late Cretaceous that they became more varied, while their differentiation into the many orders seen today took place only after the extinction of the dinosaurs at the very end of the Cretaceous. Thus in the Late Cretaceous there was only one order and family of marsupials, with nine known genera, and four orders of placental mammal, with five families and eight known genera. But by the Late Paleocene (only 10 million years later) there were now two families and 11 genera of marsupials, and 18 orders, 44 families and over 80 genera of placentals.

The influence of the continental break-up is seen at the largest scale in its effect on the distribution of the marsupials. These more primitive mammals (whose young leave the uterus at a very early stage and then complete their development in the mother's pouch) were apparently the first to appear—probably some time in the Middle Cretaceous. Later, the more advanced mammals, the placentals (in which the whole period of embryonic development takes place in the uterus), underwent a rapid period of evolution into many types, which spread over most of the world and virtually replaced the marsupials.

Had the placentals spread to every corner of the world before the break-up of the supercontinents, then the marsupials would almost certainly have been entirely wiped out. Instead, the marsupials survived on different continents for different lengths of time, suggesting that the great evolutionary expansion of the placentals occurred after the supercontinents had started to break up.

The earliest placentals are known from the Late Cretaceous of Asia and some of them, like the contemporary Asian dinosaurs, spread to western North America. The earliest marsupials, on the other hand, are known from the Late Cretaceous of both North and South America. Though it is impossible to be sure of the truth, the simplest explanation of the final pattern of distribution of the two groups is to assume that marsupials evolved somewhere in the South America–Antarctica–Australia chain of continents (cf. Fig. 6.6e) and dispersed through all three of these continents. They also spread northwards to North America, presumably over the same route used by the Late Cretaceous invasion of dinosaurs from North America to South America. In North America, these marsupials met placentals that had dispersed to that continent from Asia. Some of these placentals then continued southwards, again over the island link, to South America, but they did not follow the marsupials to Australia. They were presumably prevented from doing so by some geographic change, the most likely being that the sea had severed the narrow connection between South America and Antarctica. Finally, Australia and Antarctica separated in the Middle Eocene, and Antarctica moved to the circumpolar position that has rendered it virtually devoid of life.

The Cenozoic history of the mammalian faunas of the different continents can now be outlined with some confidence, as follows.[9]

Australia   After it had received marsupials (and presumably mono-tremes also), Australia remained unconnected with the other land-masses, but rats and bats (both placental groups) eventually reached it along the stepping-stones of islands from south-east Asia. Man has in the last few thousand years introduced the dog and, even more recently, several other placentals, including the rabbit. Apart from these, Australia has no placental mammals. As a result, it still retains a marsupial fauna which has been able, over many millions of years, to radiate into a great variety of forms, occupying the niches that placentals have filled everywhere else. Marsupial equivalents of rats, mice, squirrels, jerboas, moles, badgers, ant-eaters, rabbits, cats, wolves and bears all exist, and look superficially very like their placental counterparts. Only the place of herbivorous placental ungulates (the hoofed mammals, such as rhinoceroses, horses and deer) has been taken by marsupials that look quite unlike them—this niche is occupied by the kangaroos and wallabies.

Since Australia reached its present position, its marsupial fauna has spread westward along the chain of islands toward south-east Asia. Some placental mammals of the Oriental region have similarly spread eastward along these islands, until there is a little overlap of the two faunas in the region between Java and New Guinea. The line of separation ('Wallace's line') between the Australian zoogeographic region and the Oriental region (India and south-east Asia) is not, therefore, sharp and precise, but it is usually drawn near the edge of the continental shelf of south-east Asia (Fig. 7.2)

South America   The Early Cenozoic (Paleocene) mammal fauna of South America (the Neotropical region) was characterized by marsupials and by two types of placental: peculiar early ungulates, and edentates.[10] (The ancestors of these ungulates, and of the marsupials, were already present in the continent by the Late Cretaceous). These three groups were joined in the Late Eocene or Early Oligocene by caviomorph rodents and by New World monkeys. The fact that close relatives of these two groups are found only in Africa has led some workers[11] to suggest that they entered South America across a then-narrower South Atlantic, perhaps by way of a chain of volcanic islands along the mid-Atlantic ridge. Other workers[12] consider it more likely that these groups were once widely spread, and entered South America from North America. The question is still unresolved.

Both these later-arriving placental groups still survive in South America. But though the earlier, Paleocene, marsupials and placentals of that continent radiated into a variety of forms, few of these have survived— among the placentals, only the armadillos, tree-sloths and ant-eaters, and a few marsupials such as the opossum. The rest, including all the primitive South American ungulates (such as *Thoatherium* and *Toxodon*), were unable to survive the competition from the more advanced placentals that entered South America when, toward the end of the Pliocene, it at last became permanently connected with the rest of the world via the new Panama Isthmus to North America. Most of this narrow bridge between the continents consists of tropical lowlands, similar to those of South America, and has therefore been colonized mainly by South American animals. The division between the faunal regions of South America (the Neotropical region) and North America (the Nearctic region) lies just south of the cool Mexican Plateau, which these South American tropical animals have been unable to colonize.

Except in Australia and South America, competition from the more advanced placentals that evolved later in the Cenozoic led gradually to the complete extinction of the marsupials; in North America and Eurasia they did not survive beyond the Miocene. The continued splitting of the continents during the Cenozoic was therefore not the main factor in differentiating the faunas of North America, Eurasia, Africa and India. Instead, as well shall see, it was the gradually cooling climate of the northern continents (due partly to their movement towards the North Pole) that caused the great difference between the faunas of all these continents.

Old World tropics—the Oriental and African regions The Oriental region includes both south-east Asia (which may always have been part of Laurasia) and India (originally part of Gondwanaland). Unfortunately, the mammal fauna of India is known only after it became connected with Asia in the Paleocene and was invaded by the Asian tropical fauna.

The early Cenozoic faunas of Africa, on the other hand, are better known,[13] though even here the record only begins with the Late Eocene to Early Oligocene fauna of the Fayum, Egypt. This fauna contains two different groups of placental. One group consists of four endemic orders of primitive ungulate—elephants, hyracoids (conies), sirenians (sea cows) and the extinct embrithopods. These are the descendants of an early ungulate stock which managed to enter Africa from Europe in the Paleocene or Early Eocene, probably across a shallow Mediterranean-like sea which kept out the other early placentals. The other group of Fayum placentals had apparently entered Africa only recently; this includes artiodactyls, creodonts, insectivores, rodents, and also the earliest members of the anthropoid primate line (apes and man), whose later evolution was centred in Africa. Considerable interchange with Eurasia took place in the Miocene, and new endemic African forms evolved, such as Cape golden moles, tenrecs and elephant shrews.

Because the African and Oriental regions are the only two Old World areas in which tropical mammals can exist today, it is not surprising to find a number of similarities between their faunas. Primitive primates such as the lemurs and lorises, as well as Old World monkeys and porcupines, apes, rhinoceroses, elephants, and the pangolin (*Manis*), are all found exclusively in these two areas. But in nearly every case each group is represented by genera different in the two areas. For example, the African rhino, elephant and porcupine all belong to genera different from those found in the Oriental region. Similarly, the lemurs of Madagascar and the chimpanzees and gorillas of Africa are not found in the Oriental region, where these groups are represented by the lorises and by the orang-utan and gibbon. The two regions are, perhaps, sufficiently far apart for these differences to be expected, even if animals could have roamed freely through tropical forests all the way from western Africa to India. In fact, the appearance of deserts in North Africa and the Middle East has separated these two Old World tropical faunas, which will probably become increasingly different from one another.

The Late Cenozoic changes in East Africa (see p. 180) led to the forests of that region being replaced by woodland or bushland with a ground-cover of herbs and grass. (The replacement of this environment by the dry grasslands called savannah is probably a result of man's activities—over-grazing, cultivation and clearance by fire.[14]) The huge herds of browsing and grazing ungulates that now live in that area, such as the many types of buck (impala, gazelle, gnu, antelope, and others), giraffes, buffalo, zebra and wart-hogs, are now thought of as the 'typical' fauna of Africa. But in reality these are late-comers to the African scene; their ancestors are not known in Africa until the Middle Miocene. The appearance of this drier region has helped to increase the isolation of the original forest fauna of Africa from its Indian relatives. This forest fauna is now restricted to western and west central Africa, and to Madagascar, which was linked to Africa in the early Cenozoic, though it is now separated from the mainland by 240 miles of sea. Perhaps while still joined to Africa, Madagascar received a forest fauna of primitive members of several groups (primates, insectivores, rodents and carnivores) that still survive there in isolation, although some species are now very rare.

Holarctic region—North America and Eurasia   The faunas of Eurasia (the Palaearctic region) and North America (the Nearctic region) are in many ways very similar to one another, and are sometimes considered as a single 'Holarctic' region. Their similarities are due partly to their climate—they include nearly all the temperate and cold regions of the animal and plant world—and partly to the fact that, for much of their history, it has been possible for animals to migrate from one to the other.

North America, Europe, and Asia were connected in two different patterns in the Tertiary.

Until at least the end of the Early Eocene, the North Atlantic had not yet joined the Arctic Ocean, and North America was still directly connected to Europe via Greenland and Scandinavia. Much of the early evolution of placentals appears to have taken place in this Euramerican continent, in which there is a rich series of Late Cretaceous and Early Cenozoic deposits containing fossil mammals. The primates, rodents, bats, artiodactyls, perissodactyls, Carnivora and modern insectivores are all known first from that area.[9] Though the European Cenozoic fauna is not known until the Late Paleocene, it is then very similar to that of North America; nearly all the European families are also known in North America, and some genera are found in both continents. On the other hand, a number of North American Late Paleocene families are unknown in Europe, and the climate of the northern connection between the two continents appears to have acted as a filter. Asia during this time was isolated from both Europe and North America.

The second pattern of relationship between the northern continents began in the Middle Eocene. The North Atlantic now separated Europe from North America, and such new European groups as palaeothere horses and primitive relatives of the camel could not cross to North America. On the other hand, the drying-up of the Obik Sea now allowed the European fauna direct entry into Asia. At the same time, the climate was warmer than in the Late Eocene, so that a greater variety of mammals was able to enter Asia from North America via the Bering connection.

This Bering area was now the only link between Eurasia and North America, and from henceforth it was climate, not continental movements, that determined the faunal relationships between these two continents. When the climate became cool, as in the Early Oligocene, few mammals crossed. When it improved again a little later in the Oligocene, a number of Asian mammals dispersed to North America; some of these had evolved within Eurasia, while others had dispersed to that continent from Africa. The final climatic deterioration in the Bering region began in Middle Miocene times. From then on, most of the mammals that dispersed were large forms and, even more significantly, types which are tolerant of cooler temperatures—such warmth-loving forms as apes and giraffes could not reach North America. This climatically based exclusion became progressively more restrictive, until in the Pleistocene only such hardy forms as the mammoth, bison, mountain sheep, mountain goat, musk-ox and man himself were able to cross. The final break between Siberia and Alaska took place 13 000 to 14 000 years ago.

Despite the long history of intermittent connection between the Nearctic and Palaearctic regions, each has certain groups of animals that have never existed in the other one, and also groups that did reach both regions, but became extinct in one and were never replaced by subsequent colonization from the other. Pronghorn antelopes, pocket gophers and pocket mice, and sewellels (the last three groups are all rodents) are unknown in the Palaearctic region, whereas hedgehogs, wild pigs and murid rodents (typical mice and rats) are absent from the Nearctic region. The domestic pig has been introduced to North America, as have mice and rats at various times. The horse became extinct in the Americas during the Pleistocene Period, but had crossed the Bering connection to Eurasia. Horses were therefore unknown to the American Indians until they were introduced by the Spanish *conquistadors* in the 16th century.

Both continents were stripped of virtually all tropical and subtropical animals and plants by the Pleistocene Ice Ages. This happened so recently that the faunas and floras have as yet had no time to develop any new, characteristic groups. Since they also have no old relict groups, such as the marsupials, it is the poverty and the hardiness of their faunas that distinguishes them from those of other regions. Many groups of animals are absent altogether and, of the groups that are present, only the more hardy members have been able to survive. Even these become progressively fewer toward the colder Arctic latitudes. In North America there is, in addition, a similar thinning-out of the fauna in the higher, colder zones of the Rocky Mountains. This is a general feature of the fauna and flora of high mountains, as described in Chapter 2.

The Palaearctic fauna was almost completely islolated from the warmer lands to the south by the Himalayas and by the deserts of North Africa and southern Asia, and has therefore received hardly any infiltrators to add variety. The Nearctic region, on the other hand, is linked by the Panama Isthmus to South America, from which some animals have been able to spread. For example, the opossum, armadillo and New World porcupine have colonized North America, as have a number of birds, such as the humming birds, mocking birds and New World vultures.

Mammals—the final patterns   The result of all the processes of evolutionary change and of dispersal at different times and by different routes has been that several patterns of distribution can be seen among the orders of mammal. The pattern in the Late Cenozoic Miocene–Pliocene Epochs is shown in Figure 7.3. The final pattern found today is slightly different from this, because of the extinction of elephants in the Palaearctic and Nearctic regions during the Pleistocene, and because of the dispersal of edentates and marsupials to the Nearctic via the Panama land bridge. The final total of orders for each region takes account of these changes. The last line of Figure 7.3 also shows the total number of terrestrial families of mammal in each region; these figures therefore exclude whales, sirenians, pinnipedes (seals, etc.), bats, and also man and his domestic passengers (such as the dingo and rabbit in Australia).

Within each order of mammal, the individual families show considerable variations in their success at dispersal. A few have been extremely successful. Nine families have dispersed to all except the Australian region: soricids (shrews), sciurids (squirrels, chipmunks, marmots), cricetids (hamsters, lemmings, voles, field-mice), leporids (hares and rabbits), cervids (deer), ursids (bears), canids (dogs), felids (cats), and mustelids (weasels, badgers, skunks, etc.). In addition, the bovids (cattle, sheep,

	Africa	Orient	Pal.	Nearc.	Neotrop.	Austr.
Rodents	✓	✓	✓	✓	✓	✓
Insectivores, Carnivores, Lagomorphs	✓	✓	✓	✓	✓	
Perissodactyls, Artiodactyls, elephants	✓	✓	✓	✓	✓	
Primates	✓	✓	✓		✓	
Pangolins	✓	✓				
Conies, elephant-shrews, aardvarks	✓					
Edentates					✓	
Marsupials					✓	✓
Monotremes						✓
Total number of orders today	12	9	7	8	9	3
Total number of terrestrial families today	44	31	29	23	32	11

Figure 7.3. The distribution of the orders of terrestrial mammals during the late Cenozoic (Miocene–Pliocene). The final total of orders also takes account of Quaternary extinctions and dispersals (see text).

impala, eland, etc.) have dispersed to all except the Neotropical and Australian regions, and the murids (typical rats and mice) have dispersed to all except the Neotropical and Nearctic regions. This group of 11 families can conveniently be called 'the wanderers'. Their inclusion in any analysis of the patterns of distribution of the living families of terrestrial mammal tends to blur the underlying patterns of relationship of these zoogeographic regions. These 'wanderers' have therefore been excluded from Figure 7.4, which shows the distribution of the remaining 79

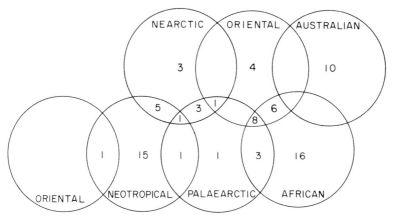

Figure 7.4. Venn diagram showing the inter-relationships of the families of terrestrial mammal of the six zoogeographic regions, excluding the 11 'wandering' families.

families. The Oriental region is shown twice, so that the single family shared with the Neotropical region (the relict distribution of camelids) can be included.

As can be seen from Figure 7.4, the majority of all the families of terrestrial mammal (51 out of 90, i.e. 57 per cent) are endemic to one region or another. The degree of endemicity of the mammals in each of the different regions is calculated in Figure 7.5. (It is worth noting that the rodents, the most successful of all the orders of mammal, contribute 19 of these endemic families: two Nearctic, one Palaearctic, ten Neotropical and six African.) It is clear from Figures 7.4 and 7.5 that the degree of distinctiveness of the six zoogeographic regions of today, if judged by the endemicity of their mammals, varies greatly. These figures are the resultant of three main factors: isolation, climate, and ecological diversity.

Figure 7.5. The degree of endemicity of the families of terrestrial mammal: number of endemic families × 100 ÷ total number of families.

Region	Endemicity
Australian	$10 \times 100 \div 11 = 91\%$
Neotropical	$15 \times 100 \div 32 = 47\%$
African	$16 \times 100 \div 44 = 36\%$
Nearctic	$3 \times 100 \div 23 = 13\%$
Oriental	$4 \times 100 \div 31 = 13\%$
Palaearctic	$1 \times 100 \div 30 = 3\%$

The results of the long isolation of the Australian and Neotropical regions are obvious. The other four regions were all interconnected during the Mid-Cenozoic. The Nearctic region was connected to Eurasia via the high-latitude Bering region, and many mammal groups were able to disperse across this region during those warmer times. Nevertheless, these groups did not include the tropical and subtropical groups that then ranged throughout Africa and southern Eurasia—including parts of Eurasia well north of the present limits of the Oriental region, which was therefore not recognizable as a separate zoogeographic region at that time. The Pleistocene glaciations of the Northern Hemisphere then decimated the mammal faunas of both the Nearctic and the Palaearctic. These two regions therefore contain few mammal families, and these families are mostly also still found in the adjoining southern regions, so that the Nearctic and Palaearctic contain few endemic mammal families. Tropical and subtropical Old World mammal families are therefore now found only in the Oriental and African regions. Though, without the three families found only in Madagascar, the degree of endemicity of the mammals of the African region would be slightly lower ($13 \times 100 \div 41 = 32\%$), it is still significantly higher than that of the Oriental region. It is interesting that this difference is found also in birds: 13 families are endemic to the African region, but only one is endemic to the Oriental region. These differences are probably the result of the greater diversity of environments in Africa, due to the Late Cenozoic spread of woodland in Africa (see p. 167).

The distribution of flowering plants today The patterns of distribution of living angiosperms have been described by the British botanist Ronald Good.[15] It must be emphasized, however, that these floral regions are far less clearly defined than are the faunal regions. Some plants, at least, are very much better at dispersing themselves than is any terrestrial mammal, since successful dispersal requires only a single airborne seed instead of a breeding pair of mammals or a pregnant female. Some families of angiosperms are therefore very widespread. For example, almost everywhere in the world, four flowering plant families are among the six most numerous: the Compositae (daisies, sunflowers, etc.), Gramineae (grasses), Leguminosae (peas, clovers, vetches, etc.) and Cyperaceae (sedges). Similarly, except in a few environments (notably grassland and tundra), dicotyledonous angiosperms are everywhere more abundant and diverse than the monocotyledonous forms. But, in addition to these uniform elements in the pattern, almost every possible variety of more restricted or sporadic, discontinuous distribution can be found within the angiosperms.

The major floral regions (Fig. 7.6) are very similar to the major zoogeographic regions (cf. Fig. 7.1). It has in the past been normal to show a single Palaeotropical floral region, including Africa, India and south-east Asia. However, as will be noted later (p. 176), the flora of the Indian subcontinent is dominated by flowering plants found also in south-east Asia. Furthermore, the maps of the modern distribution of flowering plant families recently published under the editorship of Vernon Heywood[16] also show that there is no especially close relationship between the floras of Africa and the Indo-Malaysian region; the latter region shares almost as many families (53) with the Neotropical region as with the African region (57). The Indo-Malaysian region is also unusual in containing no endemic

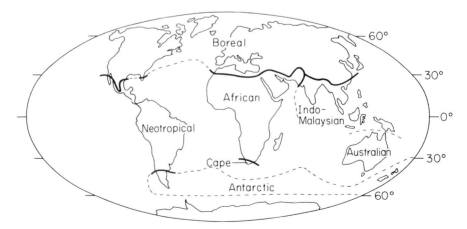

Figure 7.6. Floral regions of the world today.

families, while the African region contains 13 endemic families. For all these reasons, these two regions are here recognized as separate African and Indo-Malaysian floral regions.

However, there are some differences between the zoogeographic regions and the floral regions. North America and Eurasia are united in a single Boreal floral region—though this is similar to the Holarctic region of mammal biogeography (see p. 167). It is surprising, however, to find the relatively small area of the southern tip of Africa recognized as a separate floral region (see p. 180). As already mentioned (p. 163), the division between the Australian region and its Asian neighbour is drawn by plant geographers between Australia and New Guinea, rather than further west. But the most surprising pattern is that of the Antarctic floral region. This flora is found in the southern part of South America and in New Zealand, and many of its members are also present in Tasmania and south-eastern Australia. Furthermore, eight families of angiosperm (the Cunoniaceae, Dilleniaceae, Escalloniaceae, Gunneraceae, Petiveriaceae, Philesiaceae, Proteaceae and Restionaceae) are found not only in southern South America and in Australia/New Zealand, but also in South Africa. Despite their separation today by wide expanses of ocean, these three areas therefore share a common floral element.

The problem of understanding the patterns of angiosperm distribution is made more difficult by their diversity: some 350 living families and 12 500 genera have been described (compared with only 100 families of living mammal). The difficulty is compounded by the unhelpfulness of the fossil record, for the taxonomy of modern angiosperms is based largely upon the characters of the flower, which is hardly ever preserved. Furthermore, although leaves, wood, seeds, fruit and pollen grains are preserved, they are rarely found in such unequivocal association that the palaeobotanist can be sure which originally belonged to the same type of plant. Even when a particular family (e.g. the Magnoliaceae) has been identified in the Late Cretaceous or Early Cenozoic on the basis of characters of preserved pollen or leaves, it is dangerous to extend the concept and to assume that these early flowering plants were similar to the living group in their appearance, habit, or ecological preferences.[17] It is, therefore, not possible to identify the areas of origin and gradual evolutionary diversification and geographical spread of the different groups of flowering plant in the same way as those of the families of mammal.

The relationships between the early records of angiosperms and today's floral regions is, therefore, still very incompletely understood. However, in recent years, a new approach to the problem of understanding the origin and early evolution of the flowering plants has appeared.[18,19,20] It now seems possible to make out the rough fabric of the canvas of the Late Cretaceous and Early Cenozoic angiosperm biogeography, onto which the bewildering patterns of their modern distribution has been applied.

The rise of the flowering plants   Angiosperms first appear in the fossil record in equatorial regions in the Middle Cretaceous, by which time their division into monocotyledons and dicotyledons had probably already taken place.[18] They may originally have been woody shrubs inhabiting semi-arid areas, and may only later have diversified into arborescent and herbaceous forms. They soon replaced most of the old gymnosperm shrubs and trees, and the old small-plant ground cover composed mainly of ferns.

These early angiosperms quickly spread throughout the world in the Middle Cretaceous, having evolved early enough to cross the ocean gaps that were then appearing between South America, North America, Africa and Antarctica–Australia, and the shallow seas then spreading through North America (compare Fig. 6.6 d and e). They spread through a Cretaceous world in which, as Gilbert Brenner has shown, the floras were broadly latitudinal[21]: a temperate Northern Laurasian flora dominated by the endemic conifer family Pinaceae, with some ferns; a rather similar warm temperate to subtropical Southern Laurasian flora with a greater diversity of ferns; a tropical, semi-arid Northern Gondwanaland flora with many cycads and ephedras and few ferns, and a humid Southern Gond-wanaland flora with many podocarpaceous conifers and many ferns. The Southern Gondwanaland flora covered the southern parts of South America and Africa, plus Australia, New Zealand and, presumably, Antarctica. (Little is known of the Middle Cretaceous flora of India, which is now thought to have separated from the rest of Gondwanaland in the Early Cretaceous.)

Primitive angiosperms today are found almost equally in the Northern and the Southern Hemispheres, many families having their closest relatives in the other hemisphere. This strongly suggests that the ancestors of these primitive angiosperms had spread through both hemispheres in the Late Cretaceous, before the dispersal of the continents.

Early Northern Hemisphere angiosperm floras   The plant geography of the Northern Hemisphere during the late Cretaceous and Early Cenozoic has been recently discussed by the American palaeobotanist Jack Wolfe.[22] In the Late Cretaceous, different types of pollen are found in the two land areas: the Aquilapollenites group is found in Asiamerica, while the Normapolles group is found in Euramerica. In the very latest Cretaceous, as the North American Mid-Continental Seaway dried up, representatives of these two floras spread into each other's territory. By the Eocene, most of the Normapolles group had become extinct and the whole of the Northern Hemisphere had become a single 'boreotropical' floral region. This flora extended as far north as fossil floras of this age are known (to palaeolatitudes of 50°N in Europe and 65°N in North America), and as far south as Borneo. Most of the Early Cenozoic flowering plants were, therefore, what are today called either megatherms or mesotherms (preferring respectively mean annual temperatures of above 20°C or between 20°C and 13°C); there were few microtherms (those preferring mean annual temperatures of below 13°C).

The survival of the boreotropical flora as a unit over so great an area was possible only because, apart from a climatic fluctuation in the Late Eocene (Fig. 7.7), the climate of the Early Cenozoic showed high equability (the mean annual range of temperature being very low) and because high mean annual temperatures on the whole extended into quite high latitudes. For example, in the Early Eocene, about 50 million years ago, tropical conditions still extended at least as far north as southern England, then at about 45°N. This is clearly shown by the discoveries of fossil seeds and fruits of about 100 genera of plants preserved in the London Clay (of Early Eocene age) that makes up the low cliffs and the foreshore of the Isle of Sheppey, near the mouth of the River Thames. Of these genera, 73 have living relatives; nearly all of these are found in the Tropics, especially in Malaysia and Indonesia. The flora includes plants such as the palm-trees *Nipa* and *Sabal,* cinnamon, magnolia, and *Sequoia.* The accompanying fauna of the London Clay, which included crocodiles and turtles, also indicates a tropical climate.

Though tropical climates existed in both southern Laurasia and northern Gondwanaland during the Early Cenozoic, there is only a little evidence of floral exchange between North America and South America, or between Eurasia and Africa, at this time. This parallels the small amount of exchange of mammals by these routes during the Early Cenozoic (see pp. 165–166).

Early Southern Hemisphere angiosperm floras Because of the gradual separation of the different parts of Gondwanaland during the Cenozoic, it is far more difficult to understand the history of its floras, which are in any case less well-known than those of the Northern Hemisphere. The greatest gap in our knowledge is, of course, the floral history of Antarctica before the beginning of the glaciation of that continent. Until the Eocene, at least, Antarctica must have acted as a route for the disperal of many plants between South America and Australia. The extent of the spread of flowering plants across the Pacific (over 200 different immigrant flowering plants have reached the most isolated island group, Hawaii) shows clearly that they can cross even quite wide stretches of ocean, especially where intermediate island stepping-stones are available. So the fact that a number of angiosperm families, such as those mentioned on p. 173, dispersed to South America, Africa and Australia does not prove that all these families dispersed when the three areas were interconnected during the Cretaceous.

Two factors appear to have affected the pattern of distribution of flowering plants in the Southern Hemisphere: the fact that Africa was the first part of Gondwanaland to become separate after angiosperms evolved, and the fact that its separation began in the south. Long after oceans had extended around the whole of southern Africa, the tropical and subtropical regions of South America and Africa were still connected (compare Fig. 6.6e and f). Furthermore, the coastlines of northern Brazil and southern West Africa were moving almost parallel with one another. The gap between them, therefore, did not widen as rapidly as that between their coastlines further south, and this gap probably also contained a number of islands (like the St. Paul Rocks today) along the crest of the mid-Atlantic ridge.

It is, therefore, not surprising to find that many families of tropical angiosperm appear to have dispersed between South America and Africa, despite the fact that the last land connection between them was severed in the Late Cretaceous. But more temperate families, evolving further south, would have found their path to southern Africa barred by a wide stretch of ocean with few islands. This is probably the reason for the fact that Africa received few of the new angiosperm elements of the forests that covered the temperate regions of South America, Antarctica, Australia and New Zealand in the Late Cretaceous. These forests consisted of mainly podo-carp gymnosperms and mainly evergreen angiosperms, plus various her-baceous and shrubby angiosperms (a flora very like that of the New Zealand forests today).[23] Such forms as *Nothofagus*, the southern beech, therefore never reached Africa, although it is one of the most characteristic angiosperm trees of the southern temperate region, being found in south-ern South America, south-eastern Australia, Tasmania, New Caledonia, New Zealand, and the mountainous parts of New Guinea. This, then, is the reason for the Antarctic floral region described earlier (p. 173).

It now appears that India separated from the rest of Gondwanaland in the Early Cretaceous, before angiosperms had evolved. Some flowering plants doubtless dispersed to India as it drifted northwards through the Indian Ocean, and it may have acted as a giant stepping-stone for some dispersal between Australia and Madagascar.[24] India certainly had a varied angiosperm flora in the Early Eocene[25], soon after it became united with Asia. Apart from the presence of the Proteaceae, (which have dandelion-like wind-dispersed seeds), there is little evidence of Gond-wanaland angiosperms in this Early Eocene flora, and it seems more likely that it dispersed to India from Asia. Certainly the Indian flora today is dominated by flowering plants found also in south-east Asia, and it contains no endemic families.[26]

In the Southern Hemisphere, therefore, the Late Cretaceous and Early Cenozoic saw the gradual replacement of the old gymnosperms by the angiosperms, and the gradual divergence of the angiosperm floras on the different continents as evolution progressed independently in each.

Middle and Late Cenozoic floral changes Flowering plants provide much evidence of climatic change, because there is a strong correlation between the climate and the characteristics of the foliage. In areas of high mean annual temperature and rainfall, the leaves have 'entire' margins, not subdivided into lobes or teeth, they are large and leathery, and are often heart-shaped, with tapering pointed tips, and a joint at the base of the leaf. The sizes of the leaves also provide information as to the mean annual range of temperature: predominantly smaller leaves are found

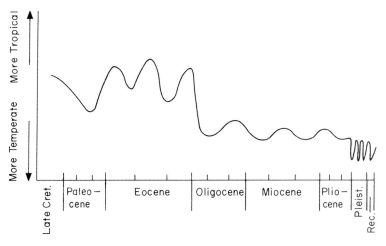

Figure 7.7. The changing climate of the world during the Cenozoic, as suggested by floras from the middle latitudes. (After Wolfe, 1978.[22])

where this range is low, and predominantly larger leaves where it is higher. Finally, further information can be gained from the climate preferred by the living representatives of the families of plant found in each flora.

Comparison of all these characteristics in Northern Hemisphere floras of the Cenozoic shows that there was a rapid climatic cooling during the late Eocene and Early Oligocene (Fig. 7.7).[27] This involved both a decrease in the mean annual temperature, and an increase in the mean annual range (i.e. a decrease in equability). For example, within 1 or 2 million years the mean annual temperature of the Pacific North-West of North America dropped from about 27°C to about 12°C, while the mean annual temperature range increased from about 5°C to nearly 25°C. In this short space of time the broad-leaved evergreen forests of middle to high latitudes were replaced by temperate broad-leaved deciduous forests. It is not surprising to find that the floral diversity became much lower at this time, for many families must have become extinct, in these areas at least.

According to Wolfe[27], the climatic trends in the Northern Hemisphere during the Oligocene and Miocene, after the climatic change of the late Eocene–Early Oligocene, were different at different latitudes. At lower latitudes there was an increase in winter temperature, which caused an increase in mean annual temperature and a slight decrease in mean annual temperature range. At about 45°N latitude, the increase in winter temperature was balanced by a decrease in summer temperature, so that the mean annual temperature was unchanged but the mean annual range decreased. At high latitudes there was a considerable decrease in summer temperature, causing a decrease in mean annual range. Wolfe points out that these changes are exactly those that would be expected if there had been an increase in the global latitudinal temperature gradient; he suggests that such an increase would have resulted if the inclination of the earth's axis of rotation had, at that time, increased from 5° to 23–30°. As we shall see, it now seems likely that more minor changes in the inclination of the earth's rotational axis were responsible for the recurrent Ice Ages of the last two million years. It will be interesting to see whether this suggestion, based on biological evidence, for more pronounced changes in this geophysical feature is eventually supported by other lines of evidence.

The Middle Cenozoic climatic change, together with the gradual uniting of the southern continents with their northern neighbours, was to be the last major influence upon the relationships between the floras of the different regions. The climatic cooling also caused the gradual disappearance of almost all higher plant life in Antarctica, though forests survived in the lowland coastal regions of that continent until at least the Oligocene.[28]

In two areas, the Late Cenozoic floral interchange was dominated by the dispersal of tropical families into regions (North America, Australasia) which had come to lack this floral component, from regions (South America, south-east Asia) in which this had survived. In North America, there was little land south of 30° N, and much of this land was in any case occupied by the cool southern extension of the Rocky Mountains. As a result, few North American megatherms survived the Late Cretaceous climatic cooling and, after the Late Pliocene completion of the Panama Isthmus, the bulk of the lowland vegetation of Central America was of South American origin. The North American mesothermal plants, on the other hand, were able to use the mountainous regions as a route into Central America, and some even extended into South America.[22]

In rather similar fashion, the Australasian area can have had little opportunity to develop a tropical flora, because it had commenced the Cenozoic in a high southern latitude and then passed north into the dry Horse Latitudes that are today responsible for its great central and western deserts. Even the old temperate flora of southern Gondwanaland was able to survive only on the high ground of the mountains of New Guinea, Tasmania and south-eastern Australia. It was not until the Pliocene or Pleistocene that the northward movement of the Australian plate, and the rather late emergence from the sea of what is now lowland New Guinea, made the region accessible to angiosperms from south-east Asia. That region was the only part of the Northern Hemisphere that had retained a tropical environment throughout the Cenozoic, and it therefore contained both the survivors of the old boreotropical flora (such as many members of the Menispermaceae, Icacinaceae and Mastixiaceae) and also a diverse tropical flora of more advanced angiosperms. This Asian tropical flora quickly invaded the tropical lowlands of New Guinea; they therefore make up the bulk of its angiosperm flora, so that New Guinea is placed in the Malaysian province of the Indo-Malaysian floral region (see p. 163). Nevertheless, elements of the old temperate Gondwanaland flora, such as *Nothofagus*, can still be found in the mountains of New Guinea. At the same time, there has been hardly any exchange between the primitive angiosperms of Asia and Australasia, very few of these having crossed Wallace's Line.[24,28,29]

Just as the region from south-east Asia to Australasia is made up of portions of two tectonic plates that have drifted together, so its angiosperm flora is made up of two corresponding components. Some flowering plants actively dispersed into the area from the west, while others arrived passively on the surface of northward-moving, dispersing fragments of Gondwanaland (as also did the marsupials). The great diversity of primitive flowering plants that are found in the region, therefore, appears to be the result of this composite origin of the flora. The view of such workers as the Russian botanist Armen Takhtajan[30] that the flora is a single unit, and that the diversity of its primitive flowering plants indicates that the angiosperms actually evolved in that area is, therefore, completely at variance with modern palaeobiogeographical conclusions. Similarly, the fact that New Guinea has an Asian lowland flora and insect fauna and an Australian mammal fauna is not due to these groups differing in their dispersal ability or intrinsic rates of population increase, as MacArthur and Wilson have suggested.[31] Instead, it is simply because the different groups entered New Guinea at different times, in different geographical circumstances, and from different directions.

As a result of its long isolation, the Australian flora is largely endemic, and has adapted to the particular history of that continent. During its Early Cenozoic stay in the southern high-latitude belt of high rainfall and humidity, the soils of Australia were deeply weathered and leached. There was little Cenozoic mountain building to provide new cycles of sedimentation, and the soils are, therefore, now very low in nutrients. As a result of Australia's present arid climate, the flora has become xerophytic, with thick hard leaf cuticles.[32] This may in turn have provided a restraint on the diversification of Australian marsupial mammals, whose evolutionary potentialities seem in any case to have been limited.[33]

New Zealand has an impoverished flora, for three reasons. Firstly, during the Oligocene, much of it was covered by sea, so greatly reducing its area and, therefore, its floral diversity. Secondly, during the Pliocene there was a great deal of volcanic activity in New Zealand, with extensive lava flows. Thirdly, because of its mountainous nature and its far-south position, its flora was decimated by glaciation during the recent Ice Ages. Though much of its old cold-temperate 'Antarctic' flora (including *Nothofagus*) was able to survive this, most of its more warmth-loving flowering plants appear to have died out. This element in the New Zealand flora today has, therefore, entered the region comparatively recently from Australia: 75 per cent of the New Zealand angiosperm species are also found in that continent. Of the 305 New Zealand angiosperm genera, 38 have arisen within the two islands, but 24 of these have as yet produced only one species each, and none has yet become sufficiently distinct to be recognized as a new, endemic family.[34]

Africa extended further northwards than the other fragments of former Gondwanaland, and its floral exchange with the Northern Hemisphere, therefore, was different. In the Early Cenozoic, northern Africa lay in the northern Horse Latitude arid belt, and was also covered by shallow seas. There was therefore little, if any, floral exchange with Eurasia during that time. During the Oligocene and Miocene these seas withdrew, and there was an Early Miocene exchange of mammals with the Indian region.[13] This presumably took place via Arabia, which was then not yet divided from its neighbours by the Red Sea or Arabian Gulf. This mammal dispersal must have taken place by a woodland or forest belt that must have covered at least the coastal lands of Arabia, and that must also have allowed an interchange of some tropical angiosperms, but the flora of the Indian part of the Indo-Malaysian floral region is still dominated by Malayan flowering plants.[26] This exchange of plants and animals was short-lived, due to the formation of the Red Sea and the increasing aridity of the Middle East. Though tropical rainforest probably originally stretched right across equatorial Africa, its eastwards extent was reduced from the Late Miocene onwards by the uplift of East Africa. As a result, tropical rainforest is today restricted to the Congo Basin and West Africa.[14] East Africa instead became covered by the woodland and bush-land that now support the great herds of characteristically African grazing and browsing mammals.

The increasing dryness of both Africa and Australia during the Cenozoic may have led to the extinction of some angiosperms from these continents, but these plants were sometimes able to survive on old Southern Hemisphere continental fragments that retained a humid climate. This may be the reason for such floral similarities as that between Madagascar and New Caledonia.[35]

A surprising feature of Southern Hemisphere plant geography is that the flora of the extreme southern tip of Africa is recognized as a separate floral region, despite its small area. This recognition is based on the fact that the region contains seven endemic angiosperm families, together with an extremely high rate of generic endemism and a great richness at species level—it contains over 6000 flowering plant species. The vegetation, known as 'fynbos', consists of fine-leaved, bushy, sclerophyll plants, and is dominated by members of the Restionacaea, Ericoidaceae and Proteaceae.

The origins of the flora are still unclear, but there are several significant facts.[36] Firstly, though they exist at present in a Mediterranean-type climate with dry summers, many of the Cape angiosperms show a pattern of rapid vegetative growth at that time, suggesting that they were originally adapted to a more temperate climate with summer rainfall. Secondly, the flora of some mountains in tropical Africa includes about 225 species found in the Cape flora, as well as other species related to Cape species but apparently more primitive than the latter. Thirdly, the climate of the Cape region appears to have changed from temperate to Medi-terranean within the last few million years.[37]

Taken together, these facts suggest that some elements, at least, of the Cape flora were originally found in temperate regions further north in Africa. As the climate of that region became hotter, their area of distribu-tion changed: some moved to higher altitudes, while others either moved southwards or became restricted to southern Africa. However, it is uncer-tain whether all the elements of the Cape flora had such an origin and, in any case, such a uniform history is unlikely. For example, though the nearly 300 species of the Restionaceae dominate the Cape flora, there is no sign of that family, living or fossil, further north on the mainland of Africa.

Their diversity in the Cape region suggests that they may have inhabited that region for a considerable time, rather than being recent immigrants. The family is also known in Madagascar (one species), Australia and South America, suggesting that it may show a relict distribution within Gondwanaland. Finally, some elements of the Cape flora, such as the Gunneraceae and the tree *Metrosideros* (known also in Hawaii and many Pacific islands, see p. 134), may have dispersed to the region across the sea. So, like most floras, that of the Cape region is a complex of elements of varying origins, varying histories, and varying times of arrival in the area.

The Late Cenozoic floral history of the Northern Hemisphere was simpler than that of the Southern Hemisphere. The climatic deterioration steadily reduced the area occupied by megathermal plants, and also steadily reduced the floral exchange via the cooling Bering region (though the North Pacific was bordered by continuous broad-leaved deciduous forests until at least the Middle Miocene). It also led to the expansion of the Northern Hemisphere gymnosperm family Pinaceae—the pine, fir, spruce and larch. It was at one time thought that the climatic cooling caused a wholesale southward movement, through the whole of the Northern Hemisphere, of an 'Arcto-Tertiary flora' that had evolved in the Arctic during the Cretaceous and had survived until today, little changed, in south-eastern North America and east-central Asia. However, this concept has not been supported by new knowledge of the floral history of the Alaskan region.[27,38] Instead, the Northern Hemisphere angiosperm floras appear to have adapted to the Late Cenozoic climatic change in three ways: by the adaptation of some genera to changed, cooler climates; by the restriction of the range of some genera and their replacement by other already existing genera that preferred a cooler climate, and by the evolution of new genera that preferred those cooler climates.

Much of the Late Cenozoic microthermal vegetation of the Northern Hemisphere appears to have evolved *in situ* from ancestors within the same area. Since there was little exchange of plants between North America and Eurasia during this time, these two floras steadily diverged. Though it has also been suggested that they shared a common 'Madro-Tertiary' dry flora exchanged by a low to middle latitude dry corridor, this concept also now seems erroneous.[22] Instead, the ancestors of the plants found today in the dry regions of south-western North America and the Mediterranean area appear to have lived in forests with moderate or high rainfall, and they have, in each region, become adapted independently to a drier environment.

The gradual climatic cooling that had begun in the Early Oligocene suddenly accelerated in the Pliocene (Fig. 7.7), with dramatic effects on the floras of the Northern Hemisphere. Though only 10 per cent of the species in what is known of the Early Pliocene floras of Europe still survive there today, the figure for the late Pliocene floras, only three million years later, is over 60 per cent; the Late Pliocene floras were, therefore, essentially modern. But the period of time between the Late Pliocene and today has seen not merely a continuation of the cooling tendency shown by the rest of the Cenozoic, but a series of dramatic cyclical changes—the Ice Ages.

References

1   CROIZAT L., NELSON G. & ROSEN D.E. (1974) Centers of origin and related concepts. *Syst. Zoo.* **23**, 265–287.

2   ROSEN D.E. (1975) A vicariance model of Caribbean biogeography. *Syst. Zoo.* **24**, 431–464.

3   SCHUSTER R.M. (1969) Problems of antipodal distribution in lower land plants. *Taxon*, **18**, 46–91.

4   KEAST A. (1973) Contemporary biotas and the separation sequence of the southern continents. In: Tarling D.H. and Runcorn S.K. (eds), *Implications of Continental Drift to the Earth Sciences*, vol. I, pp. 309–343. Academic Press, New York & London.

5   GRESSITT J.L. (1974) Insect biogeography. *Ann. Rev. Entomology* **19**, 293–321.

6   CRACRAFT J. (1974) Continental drift and vertebrate distribution. *Ann. Rev. Ecol. Syst.* **5**, 215–261.

7   CRACRAFT J. (1973) Continental drift, palaeoclimatology, and the evolution and biogeography of birds. *J. Zool. Lond.* **169**, 455–545.

8   DARLINGTON P.J. (1957) *Zoogeography: the Geographical Distribution of Animals.* Wiley, New York.

9   COX C.B. (1974) Vertebrate palaeodistributional patterns and continental drift. *J. Biogeog.* **1**, 75–94.

10 KEAST A., ERK F.C. & GLASS B. (eds) (1972) *Evolution, Mammals, and Southern Continents.* State University Press, New York.

11 LAVOCAT R. (1974) What is a hystricomorph rodent? *Symp. Zool. Soc. Lond.* **34**, 7–20.

12 WOOD A.E. (1974) The evolution of Old World and New World hystrico-morphs. *Symp. Zool. Soc. Lond.* **34**, 21–54.

13 CORYNDON S.C. & SAVAGE R.J.G. (1973) The origin and affinities of African mammal faunas. *Spec. Pap. Palaeontology* **12**, 121–135.

14 ANDREWS P. & VAN COUVERING J.A.H. (1975) Palaeoenvironments in the East African Miocene. *Contrib. Primat.* **5**, 62–103.

15 GOOD R. (1974) *The Geography of the Flowering Plants*, 4th edn. Longmans, London.

16 HEYWOOD V.H. (ed.) (1978) *Flowering Plants of the World.* Oxford University Press, Oxford.

17 HUGHES N.F. (1976) Cretaceous paleobotanic problems. In: Beck C.B. (ed.), *Origin and Early Evolution of Angiosperms*, pp. 11–22. Columbia University Press, New York & London.

18 HUGHES N.F. (1976) *Palaeobiology of Angiosperm Origins.* Cambridge University Press, Cambridge.

19 BECK C.B. (ed.) (1976) *Origin and Early Evolution of Angiosperms.* Columbia University Press, New York & London.

20 DOYLE J.A. (1977) Problems of evolution in early angiosperms. In: Hallam A. (ed.). *Patterns of Evolution as Illustrated by the Fossil Record*, pp. 501–546. Elsevier, Amsterdam.

21 BRENNER G.J. (1976) Middle Cretaceous floral provinces and early migrations of angiosperms. In: Beck C.B. (ed.), *Origin and Early Evolution of Angiosperms*, pp. 23–47. Columbia University Press, New York & London.

22 WOLFE J.A. (1975) Some aspects of plant geography of the Northern Hemisphere during the Late Cretaceous and Tertiary. *Ann. Mo. bot. Gdn.* **62**, 264–269.

23 RAVEN P.H. & AXELROD D.I. (1972) Plate tectonics and Australasian paleobiogeography. *Science* **176**, 1379–1386.

24 SCHUSTER R.M. (1976) Plate tectonics and its bearing on the geographical origin and dispersal of angiosperms. In: Beck C.B. (ed.), *Origin and Early Evolution of Angiosperms*, pp. 48–138. Columbia University Press, New York & London.

25 LAKHANPAL R.N. (1970) Tertiary floras of India and their bearing on the historical geology of the region. *Taxon* **19,** 675–694.

26 MANI M.S. (ed.) (1974) Ecology and biogeography in India. *Monograph. biol.* **23,** 1–773. Junk, The Hague.

27 WOLFE J.A. (1978) A paleobotanical interpretation of Tertiary climates in the Northern Hemisphere. *Am. Scient.* **66,** 694–703.

28 RAVEN P.H. & AXELROD D.I. (1974) Angiosperm biogeography and past continental movements. *Ann. Mo. bot. Gard.* **61,** 539–673.

29 SCHUSTER R.M. (1972) Continental movements, 'Wallace's Line' and Indo-Malayan dispersal of land plants: some eclectic concepts. *Bot. Rev.* **38,** 1–86.

30 TAKHTAJAN A. (1969) *Flowering Plants, Origin and Dispersal.* Oliver & Boyd, London.

31 MACARTHUR R.H. & WILSON E.O. (1967) *The Theory of Island Biogeography.* Princeton University Press, Princeton.

32 BEARD J.S. (1977) Tertiary evolution of the Australian flora in the light of latitudinal movements of the continent. *J. Biogeog.* **4,** 111–118.

33 LILLEGRAVEN J.A. (1976) Biological consideration of the marsupial–placental dichotomy. *Evolution* **29,** 707–722.

34 GODLEY E.J. (1975) Flora and Vegetation. In: Kuschel G. (ed.), *Biogeography and Ecology in New Zealand,* pp. 177–229, Junk, Amsterdam.

35 GOOD R. (1950) Madagascar and New Caledonia. A problem in plant geography. *Blumea,* **6,** 470–479.

36 TAYLOR H.C. (1978) Capensis. In: Werger M.J.A. (ed.), *Biogeography and Ecology of Southern Africa,* pp. 171–229. Junk, Amsterdam.

37 AXELROD D.T. & RAVEN P.H. (1978) Late Cretaceous and Tertiary vegetation history of Africa. In: Werger M.J.A. (ed.), *Biogeography and Ecology of Southern Africa,* pp. 77–130. Junk, Amsterdam.

38 WOLFE J.A. (1969) Palaeogene floras from the Gulf of Alaska region. *U.S. geol. Surv., Open-file report.* 114 pp.

CHAPTER 8

ICE AND CHANGE

Many landform features in the temperate areas of the world show that major, geologically rapid changes in climate have taken place since the Pliocene. The general cooling of world climate that started early in the Tertiary continued into the Quaternary; the boundary between the two is placed at about two million years ago, but difficulties in definition as well as in dating techniques and geological correlation leave this date open to some doubt. The definition of the boundary comes from Italian marine sediments, where the appearance of fossils of cold water organisms (certain foraminifera and molluscs) suggests a fairly sudden cooling of the climate. Similar evidence of cooling has been found in sediments from the Netherlands, and this is believed to mark the end of the final stage of the Pliocene (locally termed the Reuverian) and the first stage of the Pleistocene (the Pretiglian).[1]

At various stages during the Pleistocene, ice covered Canada and parts of the United States, northern Europe, and Asia. In addition, independent centres of glaciation were formed in low latitude mountains such as the Alps, Himalayas, Andes and in New Zealand. A number of present-day geological features show the effects of such glaciations; one of the most conspicuous of these is the *glacial drift deposit, boulder clay,* or *till* covering large areas and sometimes extending to great depths. This is usually a clay material containing quantities of rounded and scarred boulders and pebbles, and geologists consider it to be the detritus deposited during the melting and retreat of a glacier. The most important feature of this till, and the one by which it may be distinguished from other geological deposits, is that its constituents are completely mixed—the finest clay and small pebbles are found together with large boulders. Often the rocks found in such deposits originated many hundreds of miles away, and were carried there by the slow-moving glaciers. Fossils are rare, but occasional sandy pockets have been found that contain mollusc shells of an Arctic type. Some enclosed bands of peat or freshwater sediments within these tills provide evidence of the warmer intervals. They often show that there were phases of locally increased plant productivity, and they may contain fossils indicative of warmer climates.

Many of the valleys of a hilly glaciated area have a distinctive smoothly rounded profile, because they were scoured into that shape by the abrasive pressure of the moving ice. In places the ice movement has left deep scratches upon the rocks over which it has passed, and tributary valleys may end abruptly, high up a main valley side, as a result of lateral scouring by ice. Such landscape features provide the geomorphologist with evidence of past glaciation.

Immediately outside the areas of glaciation were regions which experienced *periglacial* conditions. These were very cold and their soils were constantly disturbed by the action of frost. When water freezes in the soil it expands, raising the surface of the ground into a series of domes and ridges. Stones within the soil lose heat rapidly when the temperature falls, and the water freezing around them has the effect of forcing them to the surface, where they often become arranged in stone stripes and polygons. Similar patterns are produced by ice wedges which form in gound subjected to very low temperatures. Sometimes these patterns, which are so evident in present-day areas of periglacial climate (see Fig. 8.1), can be found in part of the world which are now much warmer. For example, they have been discovered in eastern parts of Britain as a result of air photographic survey. Such 'fossil' periglacial features show that, as the glaciers expanded, so the periglacial zones were pushed before them towards the Equator.

Figure 8.1. Polygons in arctic Canada.

Glacials and interglacials The Pleistocene Epoch, however, has not been one long cold spell. Geologists have for many years been aware that the glacial drift that covers much of northern Europe, for example, is not one homogeneous deposit. In many regions it can be seen to be divided into layers, varying greatly in thickness. Much work has been carried out on the deposits of East Anglia in Britain, and here certain layers have been described bearing fossil remains that do not belong to an Arctic climate. Perhaps the best-known of these is the *Cromer Forest Bed*,[1] a dark, peaty band, often 1·5 m thick, exposed beneath glacial drift on parts of the

Norfolk coastline. Freshwater sediments containing fossils of Arctic flora and fauna lie above and below this layer.

The band itself, however, contains pollen from such deciduous trees as oak, alder, lime, elm and hazel, which are characteristic of north temperate climates and cannot survive under colder conditions. In the lower and upper parts of the forest bed most of the pollen is of pine, spruce and birch trees, which live in colder *boreal* (northern) climates. This suggests that Arctic conditions gave way to a warmer climate for some time before becoming colder again. During the period over which the Cromer Forest Bed was formed, then, the climatic fluctuation probably took the form of Arctic—Sub-Arctic—Boreal—Temperate—Boreal—Sub-Arctic—Arctic. Each climatic stage in this fluctuation lasted long enough to allow the vegetation best suited to it to develop fully. Thus a treeless Arctic tundra vegetation was replaced by a sub-Arctic flora with dwarf birch and dwarf willow, followed by boreal forest, mostly of conifers such as pine and spruce, together with birch. Then came temperate deciduous forest, much like that of present-day northern Europe, with trees such as oak, elm and hazel, this being replaced by boreal forest, then sub-Arctic scrub, and finally Arctic vegetation as the climatic cycle ended. These differences in the types of vegetation found in East Anglia during the Early Pleistocene, which tell us what the climate was like at the time, are known today from identification of the pollen from the different plants involved found at different layers in the Cromer Forest Bed and similar deposits.

Such a series of climatic changes within the Pleistocene Epoch is known as an *interglacial*. The Cromer deposit is just one of a number showing climatic, and hence vegetational, changes as described above.

One of the most difficult problems in the study of the geology and biogeography of the Pleistocene has been the correlation of interglacial deposits in different parts of the world. Absolute dating is difficult. Radiocarbon methods are of little value for dating materials with an age greater than about 60 000 years, even if special isotope enrichment techniques are used. Potassium/argon methods, which are suitable for older samples, can be used only on volcanic materials. As a result, the most widely used method of correlation has been the comparison of the sequence of fossils between different areas. In any particular area the succession of sediments can be studied, divided into local stages and named accordingly, and each stage can then be compared with those from other localities.

What is considered to be a fairly complete record of the Pleistocene stages had been documented in the Netherlands by W. H. Zagwijn,[2] and this is shown in Figure 8.2. Each stage had a characteristic fossil assemblage which provides some evidence as to the climate of the time, and a suggested temperature curve can be attached to the sequence. Estimated dates are derived from palaeomagnetic studies. Also shown in Figure 8.2 is the local sequence of Pleistocene stages described from eastern Britain by R. G. West. Because of the geographical separation of the areas and the consequent differences in climate, one cannot expect a precise correspondence between stages. A climatic improvement which allows, say, the invasion of coniferous forest at one location may be adequate for deciduous forest at another site, hence the correlation of stages is bound to be tentative unless a reliable series of absolute dates is available. In addition, certain stages may not be represented in the sediments of one or other site, leading to unconformities and gaps in the fossil record, as suggested by Zagwijn for the East Anglian sequence.

Global correlations of the glacial–interglacial sequence of the Pleistocene Epoch must, therefore, be speculative. It is not difficult to correlate sediments belonging to the last glaciation, both because of the abundance of sites and because they can be dated by radio-carbon, but earlier

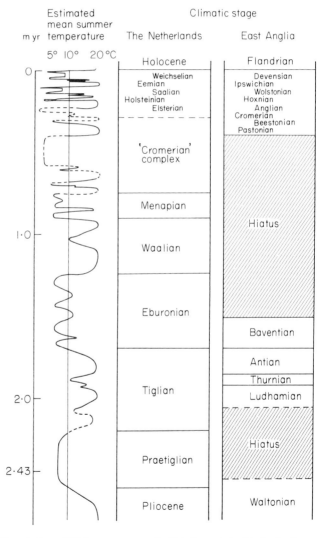

Figure 8.2. Correlation of Pleistocene stages in Britain and the Netherlands as proposed by Zagwijn. A suggested temperature curve is also shown (after West, 1977[1]).

glaciations provide a greater problem (see Fig. 8.3). Even the correlations of the most recent stages are constantly being questioned. For example, it has been suggested that the North American Wisconsin (latest) glaciation occupied the same span of time as both the Alpine Riss and Würm glaciations. Many rearrangements will undoubtedly take place before a global sequence for the Pleistocene is generally accepted.

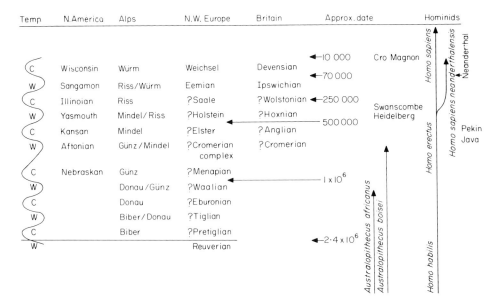

Figure 8.3. Conventional correlations assumed between local glacial and inter-glacial stages in the Pleistocene. Local complexities render such correlations tentative, particularly in the earlier stages. See Figure 8.2 for a suggested correlation of European stages in the early part of the Pleistocene. C, cold; W, warm.

The record in ocean sediments As we have seen, no single terrestrial locality provides a continuous record from which the Pleistocene climatic changes can be reconstructed. In marine sediments, on the other hand, it is possible to obtain complete, uninterrupted cores spanning the Pleistocene. Obviously, one can no longer look to pollen grains as indicators of climatic change, for these are scarce, but the fossil remains of planktonic organisms can be used. For example, some species of foraminifera, particularly those within the genera *Globigerina* and *Globorotalia*, are sensitive indicators of ocean temperatures, and their tiny skeletons can be identified and counted in the sediments.

Foraminiferal remains have proved even more useful as climatic indicators, because their oxygen isotope content can be analysed. In this technique the ratio of the isotopes $^{18}O : {}^{16}O$ in the carbonates of foramini-fera is used as an index of the water temperature in which the shells were formed. During the glacial stages, ^{18}O became enriched in the oceans, so that the $^{18}O : {}^{16}O$ ratios were higher.

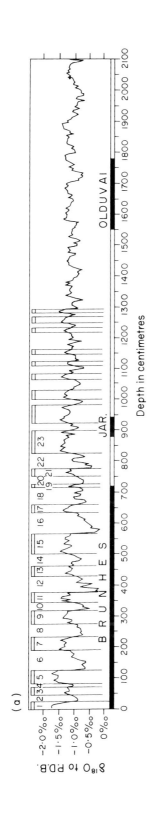

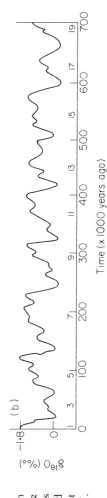

Figure 8.4. (a) Oxygen isotope curve derived from sediments in the Pacific Ocean, which record over 2 million years of climatic history. High $^{18}O : {}^{16}O$ ratios indicate higher temperatures. (b) A more detailed record from another Pacific core, covering only the last 700 000 years. (After Emiliani, 1972.[3]) Data from N.J. Shackleton.

As a result of oxygen isotope studies of a series of cores in the Caribbean and Atlantic Oceans, Cesare Emiliani of the University of Miami, Florida, has been able to construct palaeotemperature curves for ocean surface waters.[3] A summary curve for the past 700 000 years is shown in Figure 8.4 and, even from this latter part of the Pleistocene, it becomes evident that climatic changes have been extremely complex. Figure 8.4 also shows a similar curve derived from the work of N. J. Shackleton in deep sea cores from the equatorial Pacific. These analyses cover the past 2 million years and their upper part can be correlated with the Emiliani curve. Correlation is assisted by the magnetic reversals that have occurred during the course of the Quaternary and which provide a basic time framework. From this diagram one can observe the increasing amplitude of climatic oscillations during the course of the epoch, leading up to the widespread glaciations experienced in the last half million years. Oscillations have not undergone simple cycles, but have also shown subsidiary peaks and troughs. For example, the last glaciation, which is considered to have lasted from about 70 000 to 10 000 years ago, is shown to have had two periods of extremely cold conditions at about 60 000 and 18 000 years ago. It is this kind of complexity within any glacial or interglacial stage of the Pleistocene which has contributed to the difficulties of correlating deposits between different areas, especially in the absence of any absolute dating technique.[4]

Biological changes in the Pleistocene   With the expansion of the ice sheets in high latitudes the global pattern of vegetation was considerably disturbed. Many areas now occupied by temperate deciduous forests were either glaciated or bore tundra vegetation.[5] For example, most of the north European plain probably had no deciduous oak forest during the glacial advances. The situation in Europe was made more complex by the additional centres of glaciation in the Alps and the Pyrenees. These would have resulted in the isolation and often the ultimate local extinction of species and, indeed, of whole communities of warmth-demanding plants during the glacial peaks. Figure 8.5 shows the broad vegetation types which occupied Europe during interglacial and glacial times. During the interglacials, tundra species would have become restricted in distribution due to their inability to cope with such climatic problems as high summer temperatures or drought, and their failure to compete with more robust, productive species. High altitude sites and disturbed areas would have served as refugia within which groups of such species may have survived in isolated localities. Similarly, during glacials particularly favourable sites which were sheltered, south-facing, or oceanic and relatively frost-free may have acted as refugia for warmth-demanding species.

Extinctions did occur, however. In Europe many of the warmth-preferring species so abundant in the Tertiary Epoch were lost to the flora. The hemlock (*Tsuga*) and the tulip tree (*Liriodendron*) were lost in this way, but both survived in North America, where the generally north–south orientation of the major mountain chains (the Rockies and the

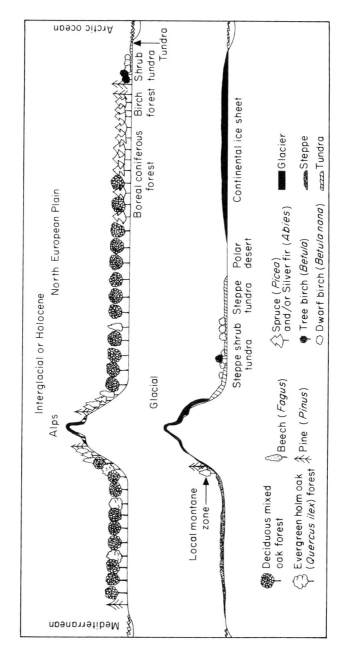

Figure 8.5: The vegetation belts of Europe during glacial and interglacial times (Yale University Press).

Appalachians) allowed the southward migration of sensitive species during the glacials and their survival in what is now Central America. The east–west orientation of the Alps and Pyrenees in Europe permitted no easy escape to the south. The wing nut tree (*Pterocarya*) was also extinguished in Europe, but it has survived in Asia, in the Caucasus, and in Iran.

Pollen analysis of sediments from glacial stages in the Mediterranean area usually show evidence of semi-arid steppe vegetation, with few trees and a preponderance of such plants as members of the Chenopodiaceae and *Artemisia*.[6] Figure 8.6 shows a pollen diagram from an analysis of a north-west Syrian site by Niklewski and van Zeist.[7] From this it can be seen that the sediments laid down immediately prior to 10 000 years ago

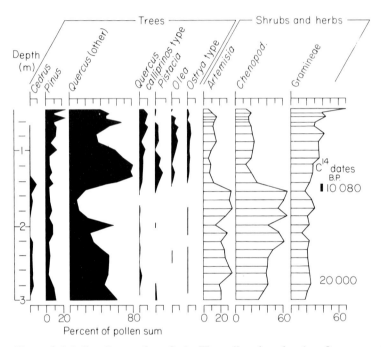

Figure 8.6. Pollen diagram from Syria. The radiocarbon date (10 080 years ago) corresponds with the commencement of post-glacial (Holocene) times (from Wright, 1976[6]). Data from Niklewski and van Zeist.[7]

were poor in oak (*Quercus*) and other tree pollen in comparison to the layers above and below. This corresponds to the final glaciation of higher latitudes.

In lower latitudes still, in the regions now occupied by deserts, the Pleistocene climatic oscillations also resulted in vegetational changes. At one time it was believed that the glaciation of high latitudes was accompanied by wet or 'pluvial' conditions in what are now the desert regions. Evidence suggesting that these areas were once much wetter comes from a variety of sources, such as former high lake-levels. In Africa, for example,

Ice and Change

a series of pluvials was formerly recognized—the Kageran, Kamasian, Kanjeran, Gamblian, Makalian and the Nakurian. Of these, however, only the Gamblian seems to have been of widespread rather than local significance; this pluvial was associated with high lake-levels at about 9000 and 55 000 years ago. Evidence for the existence of these lakes in past times is provided not only by the geological deposits, but also by the present-day distribution of certain freshwater animals. In western Nevada there are many large lake basins that are now nearly dry, but in the remaining water-holes there live species of the desert pupfish (*Cyprinodon*) (see Fig. 8.7). Over 20 populations of the pupfish are known in an area of about 3000 square miles.[8] The isolated populations have gradually evolved into what are considered four different species, each adapted to its own specific environment, rather like the Hawaiian honey-creepers (see p. 137). In many respects the wet sites in which these fish live can be regarded as evolutionary 'islands' separated from each other by unfavourable terrain. The species have probably been isolated from one another since the last pluvial at the beginning of the present interglacial, whereas populations within each species may still be in partial contact during periods of

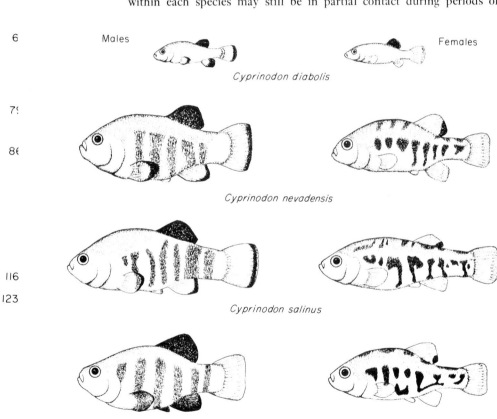

Figure 8.7. The four species of desert pupfish which have evolved in the streams and thermal springs of the Death Valley region. Males are bright, irridescent blue; females are greenish. (After Brown, 1971.[8])

sites, like the Mediterranean area, seem to have been dominated by steppe vegetation during the last glaciation, prior to 10 000 years ago. The presence of the genus *Artemisia* suggests a rainfall of more than 50 cm per annum. Conditions then seem to have become drier during the early part of the post-glacial but, between 5000 and 3000 years ago, pollen of trees and shrubs becomes prominent. At this time the sediments indicate that local conditions allowed the development of a freshwater lake. Subsequently the lake dried up and became saline with the onset of arid conditions. Thus in this case the wet phase corresponds to a high latitude interglacial. In the Arabian peninsula[10] a study of radiocarbon-dated freshwater lakes which have now ceased to exist revealed that the main wet phases fell within two sets, 36 000–17 000 years ago or 9000–6000 years ago. These correspond to the last glaciation and the early part of the present interglacial respectively. Pluvial conditions, therefore, seem to have occurred at different times in different desert areas.

Climatic zones now occupied by tropical rain forests have also yielded sites in which vegetational history during the Pleistocene has been reconstructed. For example, A. P. Kershaw has analysed sediments from a volcanic crater lake in a rain forest area of north-east Queensland, Australia.[11] The sediments here (Fig. 8.8) are too old to be dated by radiocarbon methods, but the record probably extends back about 60 000 years. From the diagram it is evident that the area now occupied by rain forest, rich in tree species, was dominated during the latter part of the last glacial by *Casuarina* and *Eucalyptus* which are characteristic of dry, sclerophyll woodlands. In the earlier sediments the pollen of *Araucaria* and *Podocarpus* is prominent, which indicates wetter conditions, but still less moist than those of the present day. So the evidence from this site suggests tropical aridity during the glacial stages of higher latitudes.

Evidence from tropical Africa supports this general conclusion.[12] Much of the humid tropical forest of the Zaire basin was probably replaced by dry grassland and savannah during the glacial advances of high latitudes. Such forests may have survived in riverine and lakeside locations. Evidence from many sources, from pollen analysis, geochemistry and geomorphology, and from many tropical areas in Africa, India, South America and Australia, is consistent with the concept of an arid, tropical climate in the late Pleistocene.[13] This fact is of considerable importance to the biogeographer, for it means that the present-day tropical rain forests have not experienced a long and uninterrupted history as was formerly believed. Indeed, some have tried to explain the species richness of the rain forests in terms of lengthy stability. Obviously, such a view can no longer be justified and the cause of their diversity must be sought elsewhere (see pp. 95–96).

Interstadials It is evident that, within any glacial stage, there may have been periods of increased climatic warmth which may, in some localities, have permitted the establishment of vegetation. Where such vegetation has developed to the extent that boreal, coniferous forest (taiga) has succeeded in establishing itself, the warm phase can be termed an *interstadial*. This is distinguished from an *interglacial* because temperate deciduous woodland is not developed. It is obvious, however, that what constituted an interstadial in a high latitude site may still warrant the term interglacial in a low latitude site. It is probable that some interstadials had temperatures as high as many interglacials, but were too short for the invasion of deciduous forest. The last glaciation was interrupted by a number of interstadials, such as that described from sandy muds within glacial deposits at Chelford in Cheshire, England. Here the subfossil remains, including seeds and pollen grains, indicate that the climate was cool, but bore a forest of a boreal type. Such tree genera as birch, pine, and spruce are recorded, but not the warmth-demanding, temperate trees such as oak, elm, and lime.

At the close of the last glaciation in Europe (the Weichselian), two major interstadials have been discovered and have been named 'Bølling' and 'Allerød' after the locations in Denmark where they were first described. In the British Isles it has been possible to recognize two distinct interstadial stages at only one site, in the north-east; elsewhere only one such interstadial has been evident. Comparison of radio-carbon dates from a number of sites in Britain and the Continent suggests that the single interstadial found in Britain is equivalent to a combination of the two continental interstadials (see Fig. 8.9). In the oceanic climate of western Britain it seems that the cold phase which separated the warm intervals on the Continent did not have such a profound or noticeable effect.[14] In the past it has been customary to refer to the British Late-Devensian interstadial as the 'Allerød', thus assuming equivalence with the second of the

Radiocarbon dating (years B.P.)	North-west Europe	Britain	Wisconsin, USA
10 000			
	Younger *Dryas*	Younger *Drayas*	Valders Ice Sheet Advance
11 000			
	Allerød Interstadial		
			11 600?
11 800			
	Older *Dryas*	Windermere	
12 000		Interstadial	Two Creeks
	Bolling Interstadial		Interstadial
			12 800
13 000			
	Weichselian Glacial Advance	Devensian Glacial Advance	Wisconsin Glacial Advance
Advance			

Figure 8.9. Table of late-glacial correlations. The European and British correlations are based upon the data of Pennington (1975).[14] (North American data are from Schweger, 1969.[16])

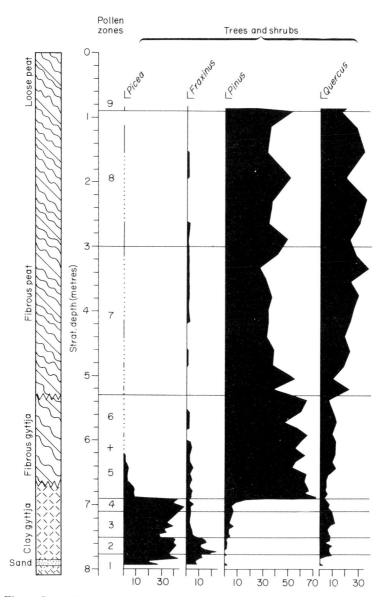

Figure 8.10. (Above and facing page.) Pollen diagram from Iola Bog, Wisconsin, showing the Two Creeks Interstadial. (After Schweger, 1969.[16]) AP=arboreal pollen; NAP=non-arboreal pollen.

main Late Weichselian interstadials. This is obviously no longer acceptable, and Dr Winifred Pennington, who has played a major part in clarifying this confusion, has proposed that it should be named the 'Windermere Interstadial' after the large lake in north-west England where much research on the subject has been carried out.[15]

Sediments rather similar to those of the Allerød and Windermere interstadials were discovered at the beginning of the century in the state of Wisconsin, along the western shore of Lake Michigan in the United

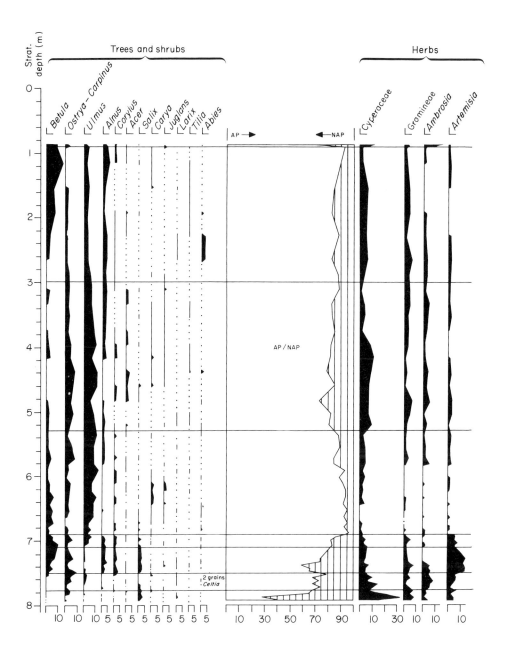

States. A forest peat bed containing *Picea* (spruce) and *Larix* (probably tamarak) logs and cones was underlain and overlain by glacial tills. It has since been radio-carbon dated at 11 640 years before present, which roughly corresponds with the European Allerød interstadial (see Fig. 8.9). It has been termed the Two Creeks Interstadial, but it seems to have been a distinctly local event in North America. A pollen diagram from Wisconsin[16] which includes sediments of the Two Creeks Interstadial (pollen zone 2) is shown in Figure 8.10. From this it can be seen that arboreal pollen becomes more abundant with the spread of forest, which seems to have comprised largely *Picea* and *Fraxinus* (ash). Pollen of *Larix*, however, does not survive well and may be under-represented.

In other parts of the world there is little in the way of conclusive evidence for an interruption of the post-glacial warming process, such as that recorded in Europe. The climatic peculiarity of Europe is difficult to explain, but J. H. Mercer[17] has suggested that the disintegrating ice sheets in northern Europe and the Arctic Ocean caused an immense build up of ice in the North Atlantic Ocean and that this affected the climate of the adjacent European mainland.

The present interglacial   Pollen diagrams from various parts of the world provide evidence of considerable changes in vegetation since the final retreat of the glaciers. Figure 8.11 shows the general pattern found in oceanic western Europe. In part, the sequence of trees (birch, pine, elm plus oak, lime and alder) reflects the changing climatic tolerances of species as the climate warmed, but it is also a function of their relative speed of migration and the distances which they had to cover to reinvade land exposed by the retreating glaciers.[18] Birch, for example, has light airborne fruits which can travel considerable distances. It is also able to produce fruits when only a few years old, which permits a rapid expansion of its range. Add to this the fact that it is cold tolerant and may have survived on the mainland of Europe quite close to the British Isles during the last glaciation, and it is not surprising that birch should be the first tree to appear in any abundance in the post-glacial pollen record. One must also remember that birch produces large quantities of pollen and that one species, *Betula pubescens*, is likely to have been growing locally around the lake sites in which pollen-bearing sediments are found. Many factors, therefore, must be considered before a pollen sequence such as that displayed in Figure 8.11 can be interpreted in terms of changing climate.

Overall, it is evident from the data that there was a warming of the climate during the early stages of the interglacial, reaching a maximum between 7000 and 5000 years ago (5000–3000 B.C.). This warmth maximum is marked by the invasion of lime (*Tilia*), which extended its range as far as southern Scotland and locally even further north at this time.

The current interglacial has also been a time of changing sea-levels. The melting of ice released considerable quantities of water into the oceans resulting in a (*eustatic*) rise in sea-level relative to the land. This may have amounted to as much as 100 m in places. On the other hand, the loss of ice-caps over those land masses which acted as centres of glaciation relieved the earth's crust of a weight burden, resulting in an (*isostatic*) upwarping of the land surface with respect to sea-level. The relative importance of these processes varied from one place to another, depending upon how great a load of ice an area had borne. In western Europe the result was a general rise in the level of the southern North Sea and the English Channel with respect to the local land surface. In this way Britain, which was a peninsula of the European mainland during the glaciation,

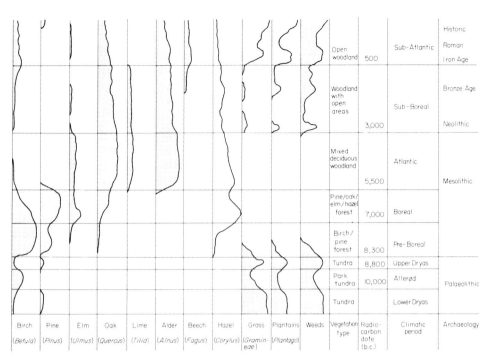

Figure 8.11. Generalized pollen diagram for the southern part of the British Isles, showing the changing proportions of tree pollen and some non-arboreal types during the Late Devensian and Flandrian.

gradually became an island. Evidence from submerged peat beds in the Netherlands suggests a rapid rise in sea-level between about 10 000 and 6000 years ago, which has subsequently slowed down gradually. By this latter date England's links with continental Europe would have been severed. At this time many plants with slow migration rates had still not crossed into Britain and were thus permanently excluded from the British flora. The separation of Ireland from the rest of Britain occurred rather earlier, and many species native to Britain had not established themselves as far west as Ireland. As a result, plants such as the lime tree (*Tilia cordata*), and Herb Paris (*Paris quadrifolia*) are not found growing wild in Ireland.

There is, however, one group of plants of great interest to plant geographers that did succeed in reaching Ireland before the rising sea-level separated that country from the rest of the British Isles, and this is known as the *Lusitanian* flora. Lusitania was the name for a province of the Roman Empire consisting of Portugal and part of Spain and, as its name suggests, this flora has affinities with that of the Iberian peninsula. Some of the plants—such as the strawberry tree (*Arbutus unedo*) and giant butterwort (*Pinguicula grandiflora*)—are not found growing wild in mainland Britian. Others, such as the Cornish heath (*Erica vagans*) and the pale butterwort (*Pinguicula lusitanica*), are found in south-western England as well as in Ireland. It therefore seems likely that these plants spread from

Spain and Portugal up the Atlantic seaboard of Europe in post-glacial times but were subsequently cut off by the rising sea-levels. It is not impossible that some or all of the species may have survived the last glaciation in oceanic south-west Ireland, but direct proof of this is lacking.

Rising sea-levels during the present interglacial were responsible for the severing of land connections in many other parts of the world also. For example, Siberia and Alaska were connected across what are now the Bering Straits, in places only 50 miles across and 50 m deep. This high latitude land bridge would have been a suitable dispersal route only for arctic species, but it is believed to have been the route by which man entered the North American continent.[19]

Time of warmth   The period of maximum warmth during the present interglacial lasted from about 7000 to 5000 years ago. At this time, warmth demanding species extended farther north than they do at present. For example, the hazel (*Corylus avellana*) was found considerably further north in Sweden and Finland than it is today. This indicates that conditions have become cooler since that time. The remains of tree stumps, buried beneath peat deposits at high altitude on mountains and far north of the tree line in the Canadian arctic, also bear witness to more favourable conditions in former times. Things are not always what they seem, however, and one has to remember the possible involvement of man in the clearance of forests and the modification of habitats. Man may have played an important part, for example, in the forest clearance which led to the formation of many of the so-called 'blanket mires' of western Europe.[20]

In what is now the prairie region of central North America, coniferous woodland existed as recently as about 200 years ago.[21] Such woodland may have been restricted to steep hillsides where the fires which swept across the rolling plains would not have burned with such severity.

In the Mediterranean region the extent of oak woodland was formerly greater than at the present day, but here the hand of man has had a strong influence for many thousands of years,[6] and climatic influences upon the vegetation are, therefore, difficult to discern (see Fig. 8.6).

The spread of forest, together with increasing warmth in the temperate regions, created unsuitable conditions for many of the plants which had previously been widespread at the close of the glacial stage. Some of these, the arctic–alpine species, are unsuited physiologically to high temperature. Many such plants, for example the mountain avens (*Dryas octopetala*), grow poorly when summer temperatures are high (above 23°C for Britain and 27°C for Scandinavia). The climatic changes which occurred during the post-glacial therefore proved harmful to such species and many of them became restricted to higher altitudes, especially in lower latitudes. Other plant species are more tolerant of high temperatures but are incapable of survival under dense shade. Low latitude, low altitude habitats which became covered by forests were unsuitable for their continued growth, and many of these species also became restricted to mountains where competition from shade-casting trees and shrubs did not occur to the same extent. But for these species there were other opportunities. Lowland environments which for some reason bore no forest proved suitable places of refuge. Coastal dunes, river cliffs, habitats disturbed by periodic flooding, steep slopes, all provided sufficiently unstable conditions to hold back forest development and allow the survival of these plants.

The result of these processes was the production of relict distribution patterns. Sometimes the separation of species into scattered populations, even though it has lasted only about 10 000 years, has permitted genetical divergence, as in the case of the desert pupfish (p. 193). For example, the sea plantain (*Plantago maritima*) has survived in both alpine and coastal habitats, but the different selective pressures of the two environments has resulted in physiological divergence between the two races.

Some of those species, which were limited by competitive interactions rather than climatic ones, have taken advantage of the disturbed conditions provided by human settlements and agriculture. These plants, which fared so poorly during forested times in the temperate latitudes, have become latter-day weeds and opportunists.

Climatic deterioration Although there has been an overall cooling of the climate during the past 5000 years, this has not taken place in a gradual way, but in a series of steps. Beginning about 3000 B.C., a number of quite sudden temperature falls in the Northern Hemisphere had the effect of halting the retreat of glaciers and of increasing the rates of bog growth. One of the most pronounced of these steps, as far as north-west Europe is concerned, occurred about 500 B.C. and caused a sudden increase in the rate of growth of bogs over the entire area. In many bogs this has left a permanent mark upon the stratigraphic profile of the bog; a dark, oxidized peat typical of slow-growing bog surfaces is suddenly replaced by the almost undecomposed vegetable matter that typifies a fast-growing bog. The German botanists who first described this phenomenon called it the *Grenzhorizont* (boundary horizon) and the name is still frequently used by palaeobotanists. Using such evidence of increased bog growth as an indicator of wetter or cooler climate is, however, fraught with problems. Often such changes are of local significance only and are probably associated with local drainage patterns, human land use, or peculiarities of microclimate or bog hydrology. Only those changes which are synchronous over large areas can be considered as truly climatically induced.

More reliable information has been obtained from analyses of oxygen isotopes in cores collected from the Greenland ice-cap (Fig. 8.12).[22] Snow and ice deposited under warm conditions have higher proportions of the isotope ^{18}O than those accumulating in the cold. Therefore the changing proportions of isotopes in the ice-cap provides a detailed record of fluctuating temperature. In Figure 8.12 the oxygen isotope record is compared with curves from Iceland and England which have been compiled from various types of indirect evidence, such as early literary sources. The combination of these pieces of information indicates that there have been considerable variations in climatic patterns even during recent, historical times.

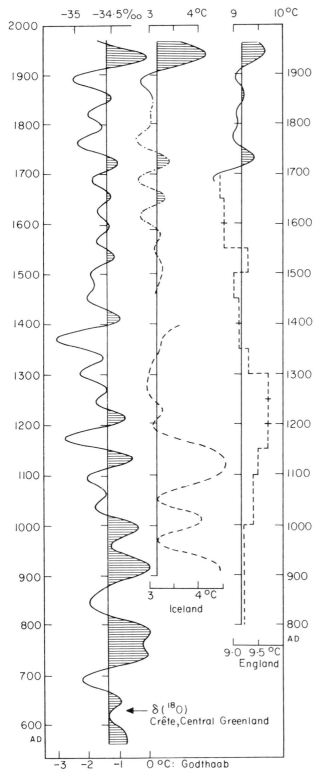

-35 -34.5‰ 3   4°C   9   10°C

2000
1900
1800
1700
1600
1500
1400
1300
1200
1100
1000
900
800
700
600
AD

1900
1800
1700
1600
1500
1400
1300
1200
1100
1000
900
800
AD

3   4°C
Iceland

9·0 9·5°C
England

δ(¹⁸O)
Crête, Central Greenland

-3   -2   -1   0°C: Godthaab

Recorded history   As soon as man appeared on the scene, he began to leave information about his climate and its changes. Early records are clues rather than precise information, such as the ancient rock drawings of hunting scenes discovered in the Sahara, which indicate that its climate was much less arid at the time they were made than it is today. With the development of writing, accurate records of climatic changes began to be made. For example there are records of pack-ice in the Arctic seas near Iceland in 325 B.C., indicating the very low winter temperatures at that time. During the heyday of the Roman Empire, however, there was a steady improvement in climate, allowing the growth of such crops as grapes (*Vitis vinifera*) and hemp (*Cannabis sativa*) even in such relatively bleak outposts as the British Isles. This warmer, more stable period reached its optimum between A.D. 1000 and 1300, after which it again grew colder.[4]

In 1250 alpine glaciers grew and pack-ice advanced in the Arctic seas to its most southerly position for 10 000 years. In 1315 a series of poor summers began, and these led to crop failures and famine. Climatic deterioration continued and culminated in the 'Little Ice Age' of A.D. 1550–1850, during which the glaciers reached their most advanced positions since the end of the Pleistocene glacial epoch. During this time, trees on the central European mountains were unable to grow at their former altitudes due to the increasingly cold conditions. Since 1700 the climate has become warmer until the middle of the present century, since when it has again grown cooler. After 1940 winters became colder, and since 1950 summers have been cooler and wetter.

During historic times all changes in plant and animal distributions have probably been affected to some extent by man and, as far as climatic change is concerned, we must be cautious in our interpretation of them. Because of the complexity of man's influence on his environment, it is difficult to tell whether some recent changes in the distribution of certain organisms have been influenced by climate. It is possible that some have, such as that of the lake-dwelling holly-leaved naiad (*Naias marina*), which was fairly widespread in the British Isles during the early post-glacial warm period, but is now virtually extinct, as a direct result of the overall fall in temperature, surviving only in a few localities in Norfolk. A further example is the lizard orchid (*Himantoglossum hircinum*), a scarce and beautiful plant of south-east England. During the first half of this century it extended its range considerably, but this has contracted again since 1940, possibly as a response to the colder climate since that time. All orchids are extremely sensitive to changes in their environment and many species may have their distribution limited by minor climatic fluctuations.

Since about 1940, very considerable changes have taken place in the world's climate which, in the Northern Hemisphere, have resulted in the southerly deflection of the prevailing westerly airstream of the mid-latitudes. This has had many noticeable effects, such as spring drought in the

Figure 8.12. Comparison between the ^{18}O concentration in snow fallen in central Greenland (left) and projected temperature curves for Iceland (centre) and England (right). (From Dansgaard *et al.* 1975.[22])

plains of Mid-West North America, and cool, damp summers in the British Isles. It is possible that the droughts in the region south of the Sahara are also the result of this deflection of the major climatic zones towards the Equator.

In the temperate latitudes we may be entering a new 'Little Ice Age', similar to the one just described, though it is impossible to predict how long it will last. Undoubtedly animals and plants will respond to this change, given time. In Britain we have recently seen an increase in breeding birds of species associated with boreal climates,[22] such as the redwing (*Turdus iliacus*) and a decrease in more southerly species such as red-backed shrike (*Lanius collurio*). These changes may be the result of an altered climate.

Causes of glaciation There are many theories which try to account for the climatic oscillations of the Pleistocene Epoch. Some have suggested that the causes of these climatic changes are primarily extra-terrestrial, whereas others have thought that the answer lies in terrestrial changes, including those brought about by changes in the earth's atmosphere.

One suggestion is that massive volcanic eruptions may precede and initiate the process of glaciation.[24] There is certainly some evidence for a correlation between glacial advances and periods of volcanic activity during the last 42 000 years in New Zealand, Japan, and South America. Volcanic eruptions produce large quantities of dust which are thrown high into the atmosphere. This has the effect of reducing the amount of solar energy arriving at the earth's surface, and dust particles also serve as nuclei on which condensation of water droplets occurs, thus increasing precipitation. Both of these consequences would favour glacial development. Attempts to correlate volcanic ash content with evidence of climatic changes in ocean sediments, however, have not met with much success,[25] except to show an increase in the general frequency of volcanic activity during the last 2 million years.

The American geologists Maurice Ewing and William Donn have put forward an ingenious explanation to account for the glacial/interglacial cycles.[26] The precipitation necessary for the formation of ice sheets, they postulate, came about as a result of the Arctic Ocean being open and ice-free. This could have occurred if water from the Atlantic had free access to the Arctic, as well it might during warm periods. But as more and more of the world's water became bound up as ice, the level of the seas fell, so that the Arctic Ocean eventually became isolated from the Atlantic by the exposure of a ridge of land extending from north-west Europe to Iceland. Isolated from the warm marine currents, the Arctic Ocean froze and the precipitation in Arctic regions was thus greatly reduced. The glaciers then stopped growing and started to retreat, causing a rise in world sea-levels once more, until a new glacial cycle began. This mechanism could have produced the alternating glacial and interglacial periods, but does not explain how these climatic cycles started. Ewing and Donn suggest that continental drift provides the answer: palaeomagnetic evidence indicates that before the Pleistocene the magnetic North Pole was somewhere in or near the North Pacific Ocean, and the magnetic South Pole was in the region of the Southern Ocean. At this time, then, the Arctic Ocean could not freeze over as ocean currents mixed warm Equatorial water with that of the polar regions. The world climate was then more or less uniform and very mild. The Pleistocene Ice Age began when the North Pole migrated from the North Pacific to a position within the enclosed Arctic Basin, when the process described above began.

There are two main objections to this hypothesis: first, there is not much evidence for such 'polar wandering' as late as the end of the Tertiary, and second, if the source of precipitation was a completely ice-free Arctic Ocean, there surely would have been more glaciation north of the mountains of Alaska and in north-east Asia. Geological studies have indicated that this did not happen; moreover, had these areas not been ice-free, animals and plants from the Old World would not have been able to colonize North America.

Other theories suggest extra-terrestrial causes for the climatic fluctuations of the Quaternary. Some scientists have considered solar disturbances, such as sunspot activity, to be important; such changes could alter meteorological conditions on the earth, but recent research has shown that sunspot activity by itself could not account for the climatic fluctuations. Another theory is that the sun undergoes a rhythm of expansion and contraction and that the intensity of solar radiation varies with this rhythm.

One of the most convincing theories was put forward by a Yugoslav physicist, M. Milankovitch, who calculated the varying amount of solar energy reaching the earth during the past million years. His calculations were based on the facts that the earth's orbit round the sun is elliptical, that the ellipse itself slowly changes its position (or *precesses*) in space, and that the angle of the earth's axis to the orbit wobbles like a spinning top, taking a definite time (26 000 years) to complete one 'wobble'. Milankovitch's investigations have produced results showing a beautifully close agreement between times of glaciation and those periods when the earth received least solar radiation. For many years the Milankovitch theory was not fashionable, but it has recently become much more popular once again. With the accumulation of more and more information on the sequence of glacial events during the Pleistocene, it has now become possible to test the Milankovitch predictions very rigorously.[27] Such tests have so far proved strongly in favour of the theory that variations in the earth's orbit are the basic pacemaker of glacial oscillations.

References

1 WEST R.G. (1977) *Pleistocene Geology and Biology*, 2nd edn. Longman, London.
2 ZAGWIJN W.H. (1975) Variations in climate as shown by pollen analysis, especially in the Lower Pleistocene of Europe. In: Wright A.E. and Moseley F. (eds), *Ice Ages, Ancient and Modern*, pp. 137–152. Seel House Press, Liverpool.

3 EMILIANI C. (1972) Quaternary palaeotemperatures and the duration of high-temperature intervals. *Science, N.Y.* **178**, 398–401.

4 LAMB H.H. (1977) *Climate, Present, Past and Future*, Vol. 2. Methuen, London.

5 GODWIN H. (1975) *History of the British Flora*, 2nd edn. Cambridge University Press, London.

6 WRIGHT H.E. (1976) The environmental setting for plant domestication in the Near East. *Science, N.Y.* **194**, 385–389.

7 NIKLEWSKI J. & VAN ZEIST W. (1970) A late quaternary pollen diagram for nothwestern Syria. *Acta Bot. Neerl.* **19**, 737–754.

8 BROWN J.H. (1971) The desert pupfish. *Scient. Am.* **225** (11) 104–110.

9 SINGH G., JOSHI R.D., CHOPRA S.K. & SINGH A.B. (1974) Late Quaternary history of vegetation and climate of the Rajasthan Desert, India. *Phil. Trans. R. Soc. Lond. B* **267**, 467–501.

10 McCLURE H.A. (1976) Radiocarbon chronology of late-Quaternary lakes in the Arabian Desert. *Nature, Lond.* **263**, 755–756.

11 KERSHAW A.P. (1974) A long continuous pollen sequence from north-eastern Australia. *Nature, Lond.* **251**, 222–223.

12 VAN ZINDEREN BAKKER E.M. (1978) Quaternary vegetation changes in Southern Africa. In: Weger M.J.A. (ed.), *Biogeography and Ecology of Southern Africa*, vol. 1, pp. 131–143. Junk, The Hague.

13 WILLIAMS M.A.J. (1975) Late Pleistocene tropical aridity: Synchronous in both hemispheres? *Nature, Lond.* **253**, 617–618.

14 PENNINGTON W. (1975) A chronostratigraphic comparison of Late-Weichselian and Late-Devensian subdivisions, illustrated by two radiocarbon-dated profiles from western Britain. *Boreas* **4**, 157–171.

15 COOPE G.R. & PENNINGTON W. (1977) The Windermere Interstadial of the Late-Devensian. *Phil. Trans. R. Soc. Lond. B* **280**, 337–339.

16 SCHWEGER C.E. (1969) Pollen analysis of Iola Bog and palaeoecology of the Two Creeks Forest Bed, Wisconsin. *Ecology* **50**, 859–868.

17 MERCER J.H. (1969) The Allerød oscillation: a European climate anomaly? *Arctic and Alpine Res.* **1**, 227–234.

18 PENNINGTON W. (1974) *The History of British Vegetation*, 2nd edn. English Universities Press, London.

19 COLINVAUX P.A. (1963) The environment of the Bering Land Bridge. *Ecol. Monogr.* **34**, 297–329.

20 MOORE P.D. (1975) Origin of blanket mires. *Nature, Lond.* **256**, 267–269.

21 WELLS P.V. (1970) Postglacial vegetational history of the Great Plains. *Science, N.Y.* **167**, 1574–1582.

22 DANSGAARD W., JOHNSEN S.J., REEH N., GUNDESTRUP N., CLAUSEN H.B. & HAMMER C.U. (1975) Climate changes, Norsemen and modern man. *Nature, Lond.* **255**, 24–28.

23 CAMPBELL B. (1974) Arctic invaders of the Highlands. *New Scientist* **65**, 507–509.

24 BRAY J.R. (1976) Volcanic triggering of glaciation. *Nature, Lond.* **260**, 414–415.

25 NINKOVICH D. & DONN W.L. (1976) Explosive Cenozoic volcanism and climatic implications. *Science, N.Y.* **194**, 899–906.

26 EWING M. & DONN W.L. (1958) A theory of ice ages. *Science, N.Y.* **127** 1159–1162.

27 HAYS J.D., IMBRIE J. & SHACKLETON N.J. (1976) Variations in the earth's orbit: pacemaker of the ice ages. *Science, N.Y.* **194**, 1121–1132.

CHAPTER 9

THE MARK OF MAN

In Chapter 3 it was explained that all organisms have certain energy and inorganic nutrient requirements and that each species is adapted in such a way that it is able to obtain these requirements within its own particular situation. Each species has thus acquired a niche in the balance of nature which it occupies more efficiently than any other species. In Chapter 4 we saw how the adaptations necessary for the occupation of a niche came into being under the influence of natural selection. Man also has undergone such adaptation during the course of his evolution, as a result of which his ecological niche has changed, not always gradually but sometimes in a series of leaps.

Man's adaptations   The early morphological and physiological evolution of man provided him with a high brain capacity, with the ability to walk upon his hind feet, thus enabling his hands to develop manipulative dexterity, and with a high degree of physiological flexibility, allowing him to inhabit a variety of climatic situations. These adaptations, together with a dental structure permitting an omnivorous diet, gave to man the potential to occupy a number of ecological roles. He could feed directly on the fruits, roots and leaves of plants, acting as a herbivore, or he could prey upon other animals. As a predator he suffered several disadvantages, for he lacked the powerful jaws, teeth, and claws typical of the predator. Also as a biped his speed and manoeuvrability were limited. This would not, of course, prevent him from feeding upon small prey, insects, shellfish, etc., but developments of another kind were necessary for the exploitation of larger prey.

Further adaptation of early man took place in his culture as well as in his body. These adaptations were of two types. In the first place he took to hunting in groups, which made it possible to drive game into situations where they were at a disadvantage. In the second place, the freedom of his hands from locomotory duties enabled him to develop the art of using artificial tools and weapons. This characteristic is almost unique in the animal kingdom. Even the use of unsophisticated implements such as rocks and sticks would have made up for many of his short-comings as a predator.

The ecological niche of early man   The fossil history of man is incomplete. We have records of a number of hominid types which are related to one another in a way similar to the branches of a tree—they cannot be considered as a linear sequence.

One of the earliest hominids yet described has been named *Ramapith-ecus* and was evidently quite widespread in the Old World some 10 to 12 million years ago, towards the end of the Miocene. Its remains have been found in eastern Europe, Turkey, Kenya, India and China.[1] The teeth of this primate give some clues to its diet and, therefore, to its ecological niche. It lacked the strong canines associated with a predatory existence and some have considered it to be a seed eater, but the sharp incisors are indicative of a certain amount of meat in the diet. Evidently, these organisms were exploiting a new and broad ecological niche, possibly associated with open clearings in the woodland. Louis Leakey, whose name is closely associated with the search for human origins, has found a battered pebble associated with *Ramapithecus*, which he considers was used as a tool for breaking open bones. In a way it would be surprising if this animal did not use tools to assist it as it learned to tap new environmental resources.

No links have yet been discovered between *Ramapithecus* and later hominids. The first of these later hominids, called Australopithecines, appeared in Africa about 3 million years ago. They were represented by two distinct species which seem to have survived after the first appearance of *Homo* about 2 million years ago but which became extinct about half a million years later. Anthropologists are still uncertain as to the exact relationship between Australopithecines and *Homo*.

From the study of the occupation sites of these creatures it is possible to reconstruct the position which they held in relation to other contemporary organisms. Figure 9.1 is an attempt to construct a food web of an Australopithecine from the evidence of bones found in association with his camp sites;[2] the predominance of small game in the diet of the Australopithecines undoubtedly reflects their crude hunting techniques and weapons. The difficulties of interpreting such sites are great, and the diagram must be a mere approximation to the truth; for instance, no indication can be given of the importance of plant produce in this creature's diet.

Unlike those of the Australopithecines, the remains of the early members of the genus *Homo* have not been found outside Africa. *Homo erectus* spread through Asia and Europe, and from this stock our own species, *H. sapiens* evolved, perhaps half a million years ago. It is possible that the tool-making facility was restricted to the genus *Homo*, although the Australopithecines probably used natural objects. More sophisticated tools, weapons, and hunting techniques gave man an opportunity to prey upon larger animals (Fig. 9.2). Fire was also used both for cooking and, in all probability, for driving game, and these developments provided man for the first time with the potential for modifying his own environment.[3]

Pleistocene extinctions—man or climate? Modern man, *Homo sapiens,* was therefore already in existence and becoming more numerous during the latter part of the series of Pleistocene Ice Ages that particularly affected the continents of the Northern Hemisphere. It was also during this time that many types of mammal became extinct in these regions.

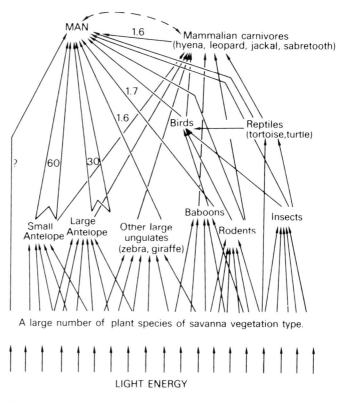

A large number of plant species of savanna vegetation type.

LIGHT ENERGY

The figures given beside certain of the lines leading to man represent the percentage of bones of that particular animal found in association with an Australopithecine occupation site in southern Africa. It is likely that man's precise food requirements varied with local conditions, availability of game, etc.

— — — — Competitive relationship

——————— Predatory relationship

Figure 9.1. Foodweb diagram involving Australopithecine primates.

Though it was for long assumed that these extinctions were the result of the climatic changes, the American anthropologist Paul Martin has suggested[4] that man, instead, may have been the culprit. Martin pointed out that most of the animals that became extinct were large herbivorous mammals or flightless birds, weighing over 50 kg adult body weight—precisely the part of the fauna that man might have been expected to hunt. Martin also pointed out that similar extinctions had taken place in other, more southern areas, and suggested that the timing of these extinctions varied, in each case the time corresponding with the evolution, or arrival, of a race of man with relatively advanced hunting techniques. In Africa, for example, where man probably evolved, the extinctions of large herbivores apparently took place before those in the Northern Hemisphere. However, it is difficult to date these precisely, and even more difficult to

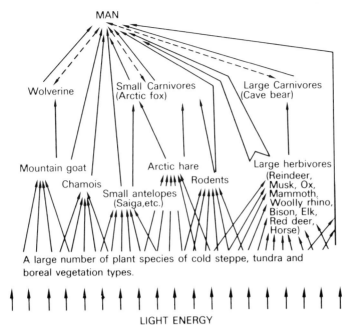

MAN

Wolverine

Small Carnivores
(Arctic fox)

Large Carnivores
(Cave bear)

Mountain goat

Chamois

Arctic hare

Small antelopes
(Saiga,etc.)

Rodents

Large herbivores
(Reindeer,
Musk, Ox,
Mammoth,
Woolly rhino,
Bison, Elk,
Red deer,
Horse)

A large number of plant species of cold steppe, tundra and boreal vegetation types.

LIGHT ENERGY

The data from which this web was compiled gives no quantitative information concerning the abundance of the bone of the various animals, except to indicate the predominance of the large herbivore group in the bone assemblage.

— — — — Competitive relationship
——————— Predatory relationship

Figure 9.2. Foodweb diagram involving *Homo sapiens* at the close of the last glaciation.

correlate them with any changes in the hominid cultures of that continent. The same is true of the extinctions that took place in South America.

It is in North America that the record of extinctions has been studied in the greatest detail. Martin suggests that 35 genera of large mammal became extinct in North America at the end of the last (Wisconsin) glaciation—over twice as many as had taken place during all the earlier glaciations, and this at a time when the climate was already improving. This certainly seemed to support the idea that some agent other than climate had been responsible, and it seemed reasonable to suspect the hunting activities of man. But the American anthropoligist Donald Grayson has shown more recently[5] that there was a similar rise in the level of extinctions of North American birds (ranging from blackbirds to eagles) at that same time. Since it is unlikely that early man was responsible for the extinction of these birds, this observation throws doubt upon the whole hypothesis of man's dominant role in Pleistocene extinctions in general. It remains possible that man's hunting activities played a part in the phenomenon, and it would certainly be expected that larger herbivores would be more vulnerable to extinction, since their population sizes would be

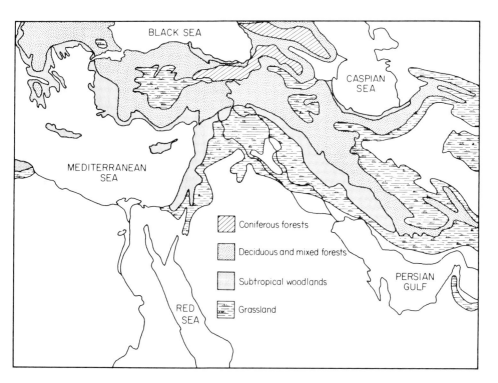

Figure 9.4. (Above and facing page.) The origins of domesticated plants and animals. The positions of the symbols represent probable sites of initial domestication.

smaller than those of smaller animals and their generation length would be longer. In any case, whatever may eventually prove to be the cause of these faunal extinctions, it was a change in man's relationship with the flora which ultimately proved more significant to his long-term cultural development.

The neolithic cultural revolution It was around 9000 B.C. that a revolutionary cultural change occurred in south-west Asia which was to have a profound effect upon the history of man and of our planet. Here, in the fertile region of Palestine and Syria (Fig. 9.3) grew the ancestors of our wheat and barley—annual grasses which were expanding northwards as the climate became warmer.[6] *Triticum boeticum* is a wild wheat of this region which may be the ancestor of *T. monococcum*, Einkorn Wheat. Both of these have two sets of chromosomes in the nuclei of their cells (diploid). Another wild wheat species, *T. dicoccoides*, has four sets of chromosomes in each nucleus (tetraploid) and is therefore probably closely related to a cultivated tetraploid species *T. dicoccum*, Emmer Wheat, which has been found amongst Neolithic remains of about 6000 B.C. in Iraq.[7] Most of our modern wheat species are hexaploid, i.e. they have six sets of chromosomes per cell, like *T. aestivum*, the Bread Wheat. No wild hexaploid

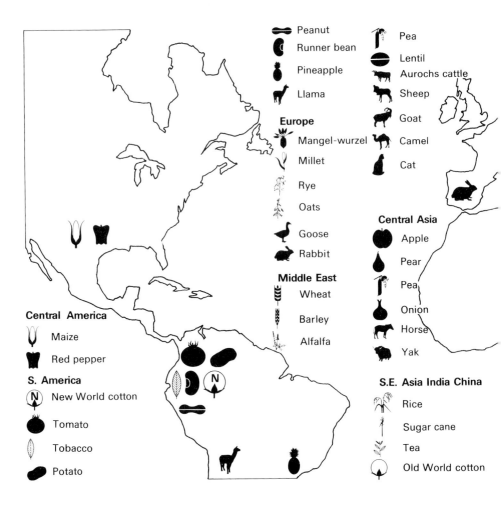

Central America

U Maize

🌶 Red pepper

S. America

Ⓝ New World cotton

● Tomato

◗ Tobacco

● Potato

Peanut
Runner bean
Pineapple
Llama

Europe

Mangel-wurzel
Millet
Rye
Oats
Goose
Rabbit

Middle East

Wheat
Barley
Alfalfa

Pea
Lentil
Aurochs cattle
Sheep
Goat
Camel
Cat

Central Asia

Apple
Pear
Pea
Onion
Horse
Yak

S.E. Asia India China

Rice
Sugar cane
Tea
Old World cotton

Figure 9.4. (Above and facing page.) The origins of domesticated plants and animals. The positions of the symbols represent probable sites of initial domestication.

species of wheat are known and it may be that such species were produced by man as a result of crossing a tetraploid wheat with a diploid grass and then a doubling of chromosomes occurring. Such hexaploid species appeared much later.

Other wild plants of the Middle East were grown and cultivated by man (see Fig. 9.4), among them barley, rye, oat, flax, alfalfa, plum and carrot. Further west, in the Mediterranean basin, yet more native plants were domesticated, including pea, lentil, bean and mangel-wurzel. As the revolution continued in other regions of the globe, so the native plants of each region were selected and bred for cultivation: in south-west Asia there were millet, soybean, radish, tea, peach, apricot, orange and lemon; central Asia had spinach, onion, garlic, almond, pear and apple; in India and south-east Asia there were rice, sugar cane, cotton and banana. Maize, New World cotton, sisal and red pepper were originally found in Mexico

214   *The Mark of Man*

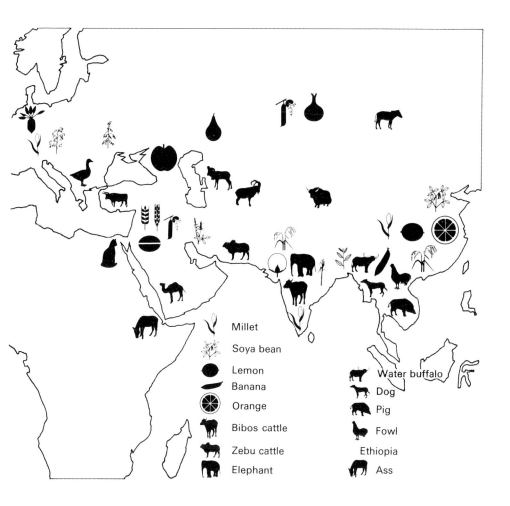

Millet

Soya bean

Lemon

Banana

Orange

Bibos cattle

Zebu cattle

Elephant

Water buffalo

Dog

Pig

Fowl

Ethiopia

Ass

and the rest of Central America, while tomato, potato, common tobacco, peanut and pineapple first grew in South America.

In some cases there may have been independent cultivations of the same or similar species in different parts of the world. Thus Emmer Wheat may well have originated quite independently in the Middle East and in Ethiopia.

The question of the origins of cultivated cotton has posed many problems.[8] Cultivated cotton has been known for many millennia in Asia and in Central America. The types of cotton growing in these two regions, however, differ much in their genetical constitution. The New World cotton is a tetraploid species of *Gossypium*, having a chromosomal complement which can be represented AADD. The Asiatic species is a diploid with a chromosomal constitution AA only. Wild Asiatic cottons also have the genetic make-up AA, while the wild American diploid species are DD. Thus we have the problem of explaining how the A type of chromosome found its way across the Pacific to the New World.

There are two main theories, the most romantic of which is that plants of A constitution were carried from west to east across the Pacific by early Polynesian sailors—a type of Kon-Tiki theory. The alternative is that the A genome reached America from Asia or Africa before the splitting up of the continents. If this occurred, then wild AA plants might have hybridized with wild DD; this, followed by chromosomal doubling, could have given the AADD tetraploid. It will be interesting to see whether such a wild AA *Gossypium* species still persists, yet undiscovered, in some remote region of Central or South America.

The domestication of certain animals may have preceded that of plants. There is some evidence, for instance, that earlier cultures had domesticated the wolf or, in some North African communities, the jackal. Such animals were probably of considerable use in driving and tracking game and hunting down the wounded prey. Domesticated dog remains have been found in Iraq dating from 12 000 B.C.

However, it is likely that many of the other animals which became associated with man, such as sheep and goats, were domesticated during the early Neolithic period soon after the first cultivation of plants. These were initially herded for their meat and hides, but would have also been a source of milk, once tame enough to handle. The first traces of domesticated goats come from Palestine around 6000 B.C. These may have originated from one of the three wild European and Asiatic sheep, or may have resulted from interbreeding among these species. The Soay sheep of the Outer Hebrides almost certainly originated from the mouflon, either the European *Ovis musimon* or the Asiatic *O. orientalis*. Domestication of these animals may have resulted from the adoption of young animals orphaned as a consequence of hunting activity.[9]

The aurochs, *Bos primigenius*, was a frequent inhabitant of the mixed deciduous woodland which was spreading north over Europe during the post-glacial period. In many of the sites where remains of these forests have been preserved, such as in buried peats and submerged areas, the bones of this animal have been found. It was probably first domesticated by the Neolithic farmers of Anatolia around 7000 B.C.

The domestication of plants and animals represents a turning point in the history of life upon this planet. For the first time in the course of evolution, one of the products of evolution was utilizing the principles of evolution to his own advantage. In breeding domesticated organisms, as Darwin readily recognized, man was replacing natural selection with his own volitional selection of those characters which best suited his requirements. In this way he became able to control both the course and, to some extent, the speed of the evolutionary process.

Evolution was not the only process which man mastered when he domesticated plants and animals; he also began on the process of controlling his external environment. Up to this time man had been at the mercy of his environment from the point of view of energy supply. Those cultures which relied upon reindeer as their food source were obliged to follow the reindeer herds on their migrations. Those who gathered the fruit of the forest and the earth were utterly dependent upon their environment. Their distributions were those of their staple foods, and with their foods they responded strictly to variation in climate and soil. With the domestication of plants and animals, much of this began to change, for man had begun to create an artificial ecosystem around himself over which he would have control and to which he would no longer be subject.

The ecological niche of agricultural man In the cultivation of cereals and food plants, man developed a primary producer to his own requirements—a plant which would lay up much of the produce of its energy fixation in a grain that was both palatable and easily harvested and stored. In his goats, sheep, cattle and pigs, man began to exploit the consumer level of his artificial ecosystems as well as the producer level (see p. 68). Vegetation which provided man with no food directly could now be consumed by such animals as goats, and a proportion of its energy reserve (if a small one) was made available to him. It may well be that the domestication of these animals began with wild beasts raiding his crops. A semi-parasitic association may thus have been set up which benefited the

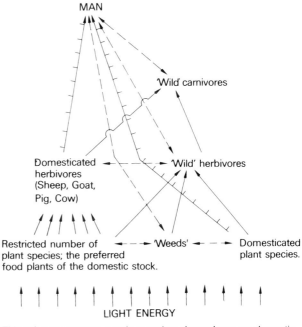

This scheme assumes man's complete dependence on domestic animals and plants. This extreme situation will have developed gradually through agricultural history.

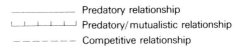

——————— Predatory relationship
⌐_⌐_⌐_⌐_⌐ Predatory/mutualistic relationship
– – – – – – Competitive relationship

Figure 9.5. Foodweb of agricultural man.

beast and which man was later able to convert into a mutually beneficial symbiosis. In all cases, the ranges of both animals and plants were increased as a result of their association with man: their pests, parasites and predators were attacked by him; those creatures which competed with them were eliminated by him, and they benefited from his increasing control over soil and season. These effects are summarized in the foodweb diagram, Figure 9.5.

In fact, many of the plants and animals domesticated by man became more and more dependent upon him. As a result of this, many of their adaptations to survival in the wild became less essential for their continued existence and were gradually lost from their genetic constitution. For instance, the long horns of the aurochs gradually disappeared and by 3000 B.C. the short-horned race, *Bos longifrons,* was associated with Neolithic people in Europe. This change was the result of constant selection on the part of man. Again, improvement in the palatability of the domesticated carrot involved a selection for a fleshy, soft tap root structure. This resulted in a higher water content and hence a loss in frost resistance, together with the greater risk of being consumed by other animals. So with domestication and dependence came modification of the plants and animals concerned, modifications which often resulted in the domesticated species becoming less well fitted for an independent, wild existence.

Agriculture and the enrionment   When man took certain plants and animals under his wing he was also provided with an additional incentive to modify his surroundings in ways which would favour these organisms. In temperate Europe this involved the clearance of forest in areas where tree cover and soil texture were light. Such changes in vegetation are often evident in the pollen record from lakes and bogs. Figure 9.6 shows the changes in the pollen falling onto a bog surface during a period of prehistoric forest clearance in western Britain.[10] The removal of trees was associated with a great increase in herbaceous plants, such as bracken (*Pteridium aquilinum*) and grasses. Also evident are some species which were able to exploit the disturbed soils and open clearings produced by man. These were weed plants such as plantain (*Plantago*) and sorrel (*Rumex*) which had survived the times of forest dominance in isolated, naturally disturbed habitats such as eroding river banks. They were now able to take advantage of the new niche inadvertently made available by man.

The destruction of forest had many ecological implications. The microclimatic complexity of the stratified canopy was simplified, thus reducing the number of microhabitats available. Species diversity was reduced, even to a single species where monoculture was practised. Water run-off would have increased, perhaps by 10–40 per cent as a result of tree removal, and this may have led to waterlogging in some areas.[11] The course of nutrient cycling would have been simplified; many of the nutrients stored in the forest biomass were released into the soil and subsequently leached from it.[12]

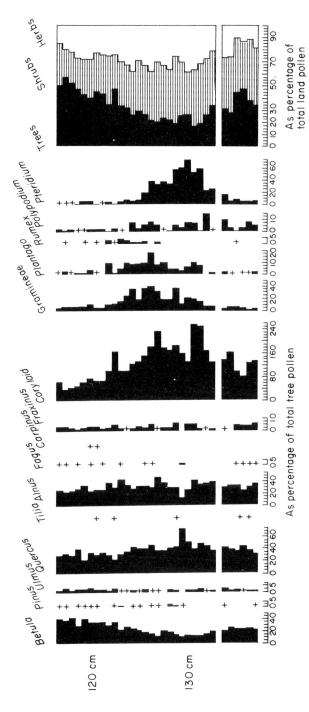

Figure 9.6. Detailed pollen diagram from Wales, showing a phase of Bronze Age forest clearance, followed by cultivation and abandonment. (After Turner, 1965.[10])

The capacity of soils to sustain agriculture following such treatment would have varied with climate, soil texture, and the precise technique of agriculture involved. Some system of allowing land to lie fallow periodically was probably established early in agricultural prehistory. Shifting agriculture was a precursor of rotational farming.

Overgrazing and the extensive use of fire in vegetation management can be blamed for many of the disasters in agricultural history. The spread of savannah in Africa, the loss of forest from the hills of northern India and the Mediterranean, and the extension of desert in many parts of the world have all been accelerated by overgrazing.[13] It is often difficult, however, to separate the effects of man from those of climatic change. It is even possible that man himself has been responsible for some recent climatic changes.

For example, it is estimated that global temperature rose by about $0.5°C$ between 1850 and 1940. This period has also seen vast changes in man's influence upon his environment, resulting both from increased industrial activity and from more extensive and intensive agriculture to meet growing world food demand. It is not impossible that these occurrences are linked for, since 1850, the atmospheric carbon dioxide level has risen from approximately 0.027 per cent to 0.033 per cent at the present day. Carbon dioxide acts as an insulator in the earth's atmosphere, and the buildup due to increased agriculture (liberating CO_2 from the forest biomass and the oxidation of soil organic matter) and fossil fuel combustion could have produced the observed climatic shifts.[14] This does not account for the post-1940 cooling, however, nor for the earlier warm spells such as those around 1100 to 1300 A.D. (see Fig. 8.12). Changes in climate are complex and the evidence for man's involvement in them is still open to argument.

Man and other organisms   There are five main types of relationship which man has developed with other organisms.

1   *Organisms providing food*   In the early days of man's existence, when human populations were low, organisms which were used as food were, on the whole, in little danger of extinction. As population levels rose, however, food animals which provided easy prey, especially the large and clumsy types, came under pressure. Undoubtedly the extinction of many of the large herbivores which were contemporaries of early man can be regarded as due to 'overkill'. Present-day effects of this kind are fortunately rare, but there is danger of overkill in the fishing industry and even greater danger in the whaling industry where, once again, the victim is hampered by large size and slow breeding rates. Even porpoises and dolphins are now threatened as the larger whales become scarce.[15]

2   *Domesticated organisms*   Some consideration has been given to these already. The development of the idea of domestication and of its use in practice was almost certainly a gradual process involving initially what

amounts to the management of natural ecosystems. The intelligent hunter is concerned about the welfare of the quarry species and will exhibit this concern by manipulating the environment to favour its survival and population increase. A set of intelligent ethics are formed such as the protection of young animals or pregnant females; a 'closed season' may even be introduced to allow breeding. Predators of the quarry species may be eliminated, and plants which it feeds upon may be encouraged, e.g. by burning heather to encourage fresh, young growth for grouse. Man's application of these management principles to hunting soon leads to a state of symbiosis arising, with a mutual dependence developing between hunter and hunted.

Many domesticated organisms, then, originally belonged to class 1, but because of their favourable features were able to enter a closer association with man, and thus their interests and survival were assured. Many organisms which have not attained a fully domesticated status have nevertheless benefited in terms of distribution and population density as a result of their use by man as a source of food. In North America and Europe, game birds provide a good example of this situation. Both native species (grouse) and exotic ones (pheasant) have been carefully managed, protected and harvested by man. Rabbits have benefited in a similar way, despite their tendency to compete with man for his own crops.

It is rather surprising that since the early days of domestication, so few organisms have been added to man's service, apart from decorative plants used in horticulture. Only very recently has man turned to large wild herbivores, such as the zebra in East Africa and the red deer in northern Europe,[16] as potential sources of protein which are able to exploit poor grassland environments more efficiently than cattle or sheep, and which are endowed with greater resistance to harsh climates, pest organisms and disease. Perhaps the manatee, or sea-cow, could combine the jobs of supplying protein and of clearing waterweeds from irrigation canals and reservoirs in Africa and India.

3 *Competitor organisms and pests*   When man lived as a hunter/gatherer, he competed for food with other carnivores and omnivores. As his population increased and his weapons improved, so the competition became more severe, and reduction in the populations of large carnivores was an inevitable result. Competition also became more intense with the coming of domestication, since this often provided the competitor with an easy meal. For example, the bullfinch feeds extensively upon the flower buds of fruit trees as well as upon the fruits themselves. When man domesticated these trees and grew them in orchards, he provided the bullfinch with an opportunity for population expansion. The resulting competition is still a major problem in southern England.

Domestication also increased the variety of species in competition with man, since all organisms which adversely affect the growth and reproduction of his domesticated organisms must find themselves at enmity with man. His policy has generally been one of elimination of all potential competitors.

Man's attempts to eliminate pest species have led to many environmental problems in recent years. The development of chemical compounds, such as DDT, which are effective in killing pest species, was initially hailed as a great medical and agricultural breakthrough, which indeed it was.Unfortunately, the wide spectrum of insects sensitive to the compound resulted in mortality far wider than was intended. Then the realization that the compound persisted in the environment and accumulated in food chains, ultimately resulting in physiological damage or even death among predatory animals and birds, led to its use being banned in many parts of the world.

Increasing knowledge of inter-relationships between organisms in the natural world has assisted the development of biological control techniques, applicable to both animal and plant pests. Biological control systems, however, must be based upon a thorough knowledge of the population dynamics of the 'pest', as early attempts at introducing a pest's predator or parasite have shown. Considerable initial research is therefore required, but some notable successes have already been achieved.

Perhaps the most famous use of biological control mechanisms was the campaign against the prickly pear cactus in Australia, which took place between 1920 and 1940. The cactus had been introduced from America and behaved as a very vigorous weed in Australia where it rendered much valuable grazing land quite useless. Chemical treatment was uneconomic, some 60 million acres being affected. It was decided to introduce an insect enemy of the prickly pear from America, but the choice of pest had to be made with considerable care, lest the insect should prove to be a pest of other plants, possibly economic crop plants. Eventually the moth *Cactoblastis cactorum*, a native of the Argentine, was chosen. This insect has larvae which tunnel in the stems of prickly pear, reducing it to a rotting mass. *Cactoblastis* was reared in captivity and eggs were distributed throughout the affected areas. Between 1920 and 1930, 3000 million eggs had been released. The insect was able to maintain itself in the wild and soon there was no further need of introduction. The initial effects were dramatic, as thousands of acres of prickly pear succumbed to the moth larvae. However, as the pear disappeared, so the population of *Cactoblastis* decreased. Prickly pear began to recover at this stage and to regain lost territory, but the moth followed suit and prickly pear now exists only as scattered plants in the areas where it was once dense.

Another Australian success story concerns the eradication of an introduced weed of wheat fields in the south-east called skeleton weed (*Chondrilla juncea*). The plant originates from the Mediterranean area, where it has many insect predators and is not a pest, but in Australia it was estimated to cause annual losses of A$300 m. After extensive tests, covering a period of three years, a rust fungus *Puccinia chondrillinia* was found to be completely host specific and was released in June 1971. By March 1972 the rust was present throughout New South Wales and had entered South Australia, and currently both young and mature plants appear to be succumbing to fungal attack throughout the plant's range.[17]

An interesting recent development of the biological control idea has been the use of sterile individuals in a population. An example of this method is provided by the screw worm fly (*Cochliomyia hominovorax*) of North America. The larvae of this insect, particularly in Texas, invade wound areas of cattle, and feed upon surrounding tissues. This enlarges the wound and encourages further egg laying by female flies. Until 1962 approximately 50 000 head of cattle were lost each year in Texas as a result of the activities of this pest. The expanse of the Texas ranges made regular examination and chemical treatment of beasts an impossibility, and the feasibility of a biological control measure was considered. Study of the life-cycle and population ecology of the insect provided a means by which this could be achieved. It was found that female flies mated only once, and were then capable of egg laying. It was also found that flies could be rendered sterile, but otherwise unharmed, by irradiating them at the pupal stage of development. If male flies were sterilized and then released into the natural population, they competed with fertile males for the female flies and a proportion of ineffectual matings resulted. The more sterilized males released, the fewer fertilized females resulted in the natural population. Flies were bred in factories on enormous scales, sterilized and then released. The number of cases of livestock infection are as follows:

> 1962—over 50 000
> 1963—over 5000
> 1964—226
> 1970—153

However, the success has not been maintained, mainly because of the constant reinvasion from Mexico. The next two years gave the following figures:

> 1971— 473
> 1972—92 192

Thus the situation seemed even worse than back in 1962. The reason for this may be explained by evolutionary adaptations within the fly. There would be a strong selective advantage to be gained from the wild female mating with a wild, fertile male, rather than a factory-produced sterilized one. The development of new behavioural mechanisms may have occurred which render this more likely. Efforts are now being made to eradicate the screw worm fly from Mexico using even higher numbers of sterilized males (as many as 300 million a week has been suggested).

4 *Organisms following in man's wake*   Some species of plant and animal have been favoured by man's activities and by his spread, having been able to occupy vacant niches in the ecosystems man has created for himself. For example, in the agricultural ecosystem there are many interesting examples of the ways in which wild plants have become adapted for survival. *Camelina sativa* (gold of pleasure) is one example; this plant is a native of eastern Europe, and has probably adopted the role of a flax-field weed ever since *Linum* (flax) was first cultivated. However, man spent much energy in his efforts to maintain a single-species population in his flax fields, and

developed the process of winnowing the seeds to eliminate aliens. In this process *Linum* seeds are separated from chaff and smaller seeds by their low surface/weight ratio, whereby they fall rapidly to the ground when thrown in the air, whilst lighter material is blown away. *Camelina sativa*, in response to such selection for a particular seed size, has evolved a variety with seeds of very similar properties to those of *Linum*, which cannot be separated by winnowing. This variety was thus assured of survival and extended range at the hand of man until more effective screening methods were developed.

Many animals have also been able to take advantage of the artificial ecosystem which man has provided. Some species which were once cliff dwellers, such as the starling and the rock dove, have established themselves in cities throughout the world, feeding in parks and gardens and returning to roost upon the concrete 'cliffs' of city centres. Here are examples of organisms occupying specialized ecological niches at low population densities, which have developed the necessary flexibility to invade and occupy the new niches which man has provided.

An interesting development of the last century has been the occupation of a new niche by the black-headed gull. This essentially sea bird has now become a familiar sight in British arable countryside, often over a hundred miles from the sea. Here it scavenges in fields with members of the Corvidae (crows) and is also becoming increasingly common upon urban rubbish tips. Until very recently these inland parties of gulls have been almost entirely restricted to winter, but there are now many sites, particularly around large man-made reservoirs, where the black-headed gull breeds inland. Its occupation of this new man-made niche is thus becoming more complete.

The increasing mobility of man has assisted in the spread of many pest species from one continent to another. In the last decade we have seen the epidemic spread of a new and virulent strain of the Dutch elm disease fungus, *Ceratocystis ulmi,* in both North America and Europe. Work in the United Kingdom suggests that the strain arrived in Britain as a result of the importation of infected timber from Toronto,[18] and the outcome has been the virtual extinction of the English elm (*Ulmus procera*) from southern England. An interesting comparison can be made with a decline of elm recorded in the pollen diagrams of north-west Europe and dating from about 5000 years ago. That collapse in elm populations correlates with the arrival of neolithic agricultural techniques from the south-east of Europe. It is possible that the movements of people, animals and equipment at that time assisted in the epidemic spread of an elm disease.

Many diseases of man spread just as rapidly, especially where populations are dense, mobility is high, and sanitation is poor. Figure 9.7 shows the speed at which an epidemic of cholera spread across Asia, Africa and into Europe between 1961 and 1972. The control of pests such as the cholera organism can be achieved only by international action to improve standards of sanitation and hygiene in the areas at risk.[19]

In a way, man has reconstructed the bridges between continents by means of his transportation systems. His ships carry such alien animals as

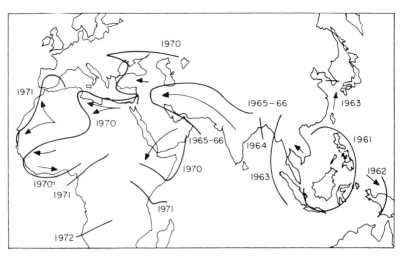

Figure 9.7. The global spread of cholera between 1961 and 1972. (After Cujetanovic and Barua, 1972.[19])

rats and ants to islands once remote from such influence, and the resulting disturbance of the existing balance can be catastrophic. The construction of waterways has often linked bodies of water previously isolated from one another, and this has opened new routes for the spread of some species. For example, Lake Erie and Lake Ontario were connected only by the Niagara River (including the Falls) until the building of the Erie Canal in 1819 and the Welland Canal in 1825. Although organisms could have moved downstream from Erie to Ontario before the canals were constructed, the reverse trip was almost impossible. Since that time, however, such new species of fish as the alewife and the sea lamprey have appeared in Lake Ontario (from the Hudson River via the Erie Canal) and in Lake Erie.[20] These species have caused considerable disturbance to the original balance of the two lakes, although pollution problems of other kinds have proved even more serious to fishing interests.

Similarly, the Suez Canal has provided a new route for the exchange of organisms between the Mediterranean and the Red Sea. The most striking movement has been from the Red Sea to the Mediterranean; about 30 species have succeeded in this invasion, and such fish as the goat fish and the lizard fish are now of major commercial importance to the Turkish fishing industry.

5 *Organisms affected by habitat modification* In certain cases man's disruption of the natural habitat has brought together species which are normally widely separated by their differing ecological requirements. For example, the destruction of woodland and its replacement by meadow in southern Britain has brought together two closely related species of the genus *Primula*. *Primula vulgaris* is the primrose, a yellow flower which is usually found growing in deep shade in woodlands. Its flowers are borne on long individual stalks arising from the centre of a rosette of leaves. The

cowslip (*P. veris*) on the other hand, is a closely related species growing in open meadows. It has yellowish orange flowers on short stalks which are all borne at the apex of a leafless floral axis or scape surrounded by a basal rosette of leaves. Under natural conditions, that is in the absence of man, it is most unlikely that these two plants should ever be found together because of their different environmental requirements. However, man has destroyed this natural barrier by clearing woodland and replacing it with fragmentary copses and hedgerows. In this way the two species have been brought into contact and have cross-bred to give a fertile hybrid with characters intermediate between the two parental species. This hybrid has the scape of *P. veris*, on top of which are borne yellow flowers with long individual stalks, like those of *P. vulgaris*.

Often, however, disruption and fragmentation of habitats has had even more serious effects upon their occupants. Some species, particularly large predators, require an extensive area of specialized habitat in which to hunt and breed. Fragmentation of such habitats has often had devastating effects upon the population levels of such species. A good example of this is afforded by the marsh harrier, a large raptorial bird of reedbeds and fens. Besides needing a wide area of reedswamp for hunting, this bird will not nest except in the isolation provided by extensive reedbeds. Because of its demand for space, this bird has suffered badly as a result of drainage of wetlands, both in Europe and North America.

Britain was once almost completely covered with woodland, yet now, primarily due to man's activity, only 7·5 per cent of its land is wooded. This represents one acre for every 13 inhabitants.[21] In Germany, another industrialized country, there is one acre of woodland to every eight persons and in the United States there are four acres of woodland to each person. In general, those countries which became industrialized before the exploitation of fossil fuel have fared worse as far as woodland depletion is concerned. However, intensive agriculture has also taken its toll of land once wooded, especially in highly populated countries. Twenty-nine million acres of Britain are under crops and grass, out of a total land area of 56 million acres. Urban areas constitute 4·5 million acres. Under such conditions Britain is forced to import 90 per cent of its timber requirement. The industralized and agriculturalized nations are thus placing a heavy demand upon the woodlands of the less developed nations.

Man's demand for agricultural land, together with recent urban development and industrial growth, has led to many modifications of global environments,[22] only a few of which can be mentioned here. For example, pollution of the atmosphere, particularly by sulphur dioxide, a product of the combustion of coal and oil, has influenced the distribution patterns of many sensitive species of epiphytic lichens and mosses. Figure 9.8 shows the way in which the distribution of one such species, *Parmelia caperata*, once widespread in central England, has now become restricted as a consequence of air pollution.[23]

The fragmentation of a habitat such as a woodland results in what can be regarded as a series of woodland 'islands' isolated from one another by non-wooded terrain. Because of this we can apply to such a situation the ideas underlying island biogeographic theory.[24] As the woodland 'island' becomes smaller, so the populations of certain organisms will fall to such a level as to place them in danger of extinction. Those demanding the greatest uninterrupted areas will become extinct first. Whether or not lost species can reinvade depends upon a number of factors, such as the distance from other islands, the dispersal ability of the species in question, and the nature of the intervening country.

If fragmented habitats do obey the island biogeography rules (see p. 125), one would expect the number of species in a woodland to be a function of its area. A survey of bird species in 433 British woodlands[25] showed just such a relationship. It was found that the MacArthur and Wilson island biogeographic model in which there is a constant relationship between the number of species and the area of the island,

$$\log \text{ number of species} = K \log \text{ area} + \log \text{ species per unit area}$$

held good for the data obtained. So isolated patches of woodland in a 'sea' of agricultural land are similar to islands in their species:area relationships. As might be expected, the area needed for successful occupation and breeding varies with species. A linnet needs 15 m², a blue tit 70 m², a blackcap 300 m², and a spotted flycatcher 600 m². Woodland reduction would, therefore, affect these species in reverse order.

What of the intervening land? Does, for example, the survival of hedges assist in the movement of organisms from one wood island to another and hence permit reinvasion after chance local extinction? The likelihood is that hedges provide corridors of movement only for those species with very low area requirements. Certainly, in the case of plant species[26] it is found that truly woodland species are not able to migrate along hedges, and hence the maintenance of hedge systems is not an alternative to retaining large blocks of forest as a conservation measure.

In this discussion of man's relationship with other animals and with plants there has been an underlying assumption that the conservation of other species is a good thing, though exception must be made of direct competitors (pests), parasites of man, or of his domesticated organisms. Apart from the aesthetic reasons supporting conservation, upon which a biogeographer is no better qualified to comment than any other individual, there is a strong scientific argument for conservation based upon the maintenance of the world's genetic resources. Whenever a species becomes extinct, the world suffers the loss of a body of genetic material which has taken hundreds of millions of years to assemble itself. It is, therefore, an irreplaceable loss, and any use to which it may have been put by man on some future occasion is no longer a possibility. The maintenance of threatened species should, therefore, be a high priority for man's scientific efforts. Where it becomes impossible to conserve the species in its native habitat because of unavoidable disturbance or destruction, efforts are usually made to maintain breeding populations in zoological or botanical gardens. In the case of plants, the possibilities of using seed banks[27] in which seed can be kept at low temperatures, about $-10°$C, have been extensively examined. Germination tests are made every year and, if viability begins to fall, the plants can be grown up and a new batch of seed

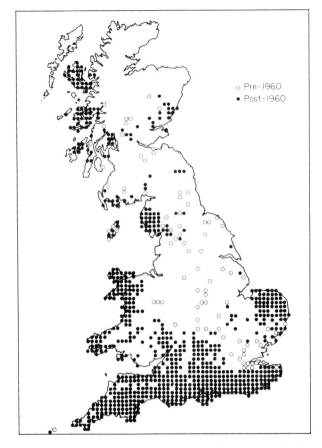

Figure 9.8a. Map showing the pre- and post-1960 distribution of *Parmelia caperata* in the British Isles (excluding Ireland). (From Ferry, Baddeley and Hawksworth (eds), 1973.[23])

produced. This allows a maximum number of species to be maintained with a minimum of effort and space. It also permits a wide range of genetic variability to be retained and yet places little additional stress upon any surviving wild populations.

These examples demonstrate that the control of man's environment need not be a clumsy and haphazard affair. The factor which differentiates these situations from the numerous occasions upon which man's attempts at environmental control have ended in tragedy, is the degree of research and planning which has preceded the introduction of the control measures in these cases. On all occasions any crude chemical control measures attempted proved ineffective, and thorough planning was unavoidable. The time is rapidly approaching when a long term view must be taken and crude, short-term remedies abandoned even where they would meet with apparent success.

Whilst considering the distributions of animals and plants it must have become evident that man himself is not above, nor is he outside, the

The Mark of Man

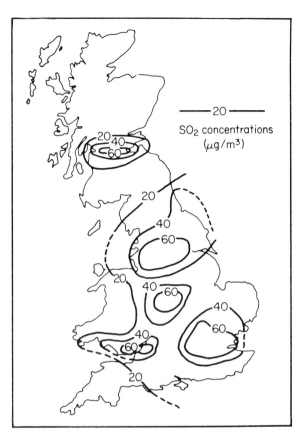

Figure 9.8b. Map showing the approximate annual mean sulphur dioxide concentration in areas far from pollution. (By courtesy of the National Society for Clean Air.)

problems which these distributions pose. As an animal with a physiology not unlike that of other animals, he too is dependent upon the physical factors of the environment for his continued existence. His cultural development has granted him a degree of insulation from his environment which has enabled him to invade areas of the globe which are physically inhospitable, but his insulation is not such that he can continue to exploit the world's resources and pollute its surface without any concern for the consequences. Nor is it such that he can continue to expand his population indefinitely: there comes a saturation point. The conservation of the environment ultimately means the conservation of mankind. It therefore demands our attention.

If we were to ask the question, what is man's greatest need, then the answer, as ever, must be knowledge, followed by the wisdom to act upon that knowledge. Knowledge of how our environment works involves research, and research is expensive. Action to conserve the environment based upon that research would cost very much more money. The dilemma in which man finds himself therefore is essentially a financial one. He must consider whether short-term economic gain and an artificially high standard of living for those parts of humanity who happen to be fortunate enough to live in the developed countries are worth the sacrifice of the future of much of mankind over the whole of the little globe upon which we live.

References

1 LEAKEY R.E. & LEWIN R. (1977) *Origins*. Macdonald and Jane's Publishers Ltd., London.

2 HOWELL F.C. (1966) The Villafranchian and human origins. In: Caldwell J.R. (ed.), *New Roads to Yesterday*, pp. 37–77. Thames and Hudson, London.

3 WATERBOLK G. (1968) Food production in prehistoric Europe. *Science, N.Y.* **162**, 1093–1102.

4 MARTIN P.S. & WRIGHT H.E. (eds) (1967) *Pleistocene Extinctions: the Search for a Cause*. Yale University Press, London.

5 GRAYSON J.E. (1977) Pleistocene avifaunas and the overkill hypothesis. *Science* **195**, 691–693.

6 BUTZER K. (1972) *Environment and Archaeology*, 2nd edn. Methuen, London.

7 WRIGHT H.E. (1970) Environmental changes and the origin of agriculture in the Near East. *Bioscience* **20**, 210–212.

8 PICKERSGILL B. & BUNTING A.H. (1969) Cultivated plants and the Kon-Tiki theory. *Nature, Lond.* **222**, 225–227.

9 BÖKÖNYI S. (1976) Development of early stock rearing in the Near East. *Nature, Lond.* **264**, 19–23.

10 TURNER J. (1965) A contribution to the history of forest clearance. *Proc. R. Soc. Lond. B* **161**, 343–354.

11 MOORE P.D. (1975) Origin of blanket mires. *Nature, Lond.* **256**, 267–269.

12 BORMANN F.H., LIKENS G.E., FISHER D.W. & PIERCE R.S. (1968). Nutrient loss accelerated by clear cutting of a forest ecosystem. *Science* **159**, 882–884.

13 ECKDAHL E.P. (1975) The deterioration of mountain environments. *Science, N.Y.* **189**, 764–770.

14 WILSON A.T. (1978) Pioneer agriculture explosion and CO_2 levels in the atmosphere. *Nature, Lond.* **273**, 40–41.

15 BURTON J.A. (1975) The future of small whales. *New Scientist* **66**, 650–652.

16 MEURON-LANDOLT M. DE (1975) Farming the red deer. *New Scientist* **66**, 545–548.

17 CULLEN J.M., KABLE P.F. & CATT M. (1973) Epidemic spread of a rust imported for biological control. *Nature, Lond.* **244**, 462–464.

18 BRASIER C.M. & GIBBS J.N. (1973) Origin of the Dutch elm disease epidemic in Britain. *Nature, Lond.* **242**, 607–609.

19 CUJETANOVIC B. & BARUA D. (1972) The seventh pandemic of cholera. *Nature, Lond.* **289**, 137–138.

20 ARON W.I. & SMITH S.H. (1971) Ship canals and aquatic ecosystems. *Science, N.Y.* **174**, 13–20.

21 ARVILL R. (1976) *Man and Environment*. Penguin Books, Harmondsworth.

22 EHRLICH P.R., EHRLICH A.H. & HOLDREN J.P. (1977) *Ecoscience: Population Resources, Environment*, 3rd edn. W.H. Freeman, San Francisco.

23 FERRY B., BADDELEY M.S. & HAWKSWORTH D.L. (eds) (1973) *Air Pollution and Lichens*. Athlone Press, London.

24 MAY R.M. (1975) Island biogeography and the design of wildlife preserves. *Nature, Lond.* **254**, 177–178.

25 MOORE N.W. & HOOPER M.D. (1975) On the number of bird species in British woods. *Biol. Conserv.* **8**, 239–250.

26 HELLIWELL D.R. (1975) The distribution of woodland plant species in some Shropshire hedgerows. *Biol. Conserv.* **7**, 61–71.

27 THOMPSON P.A. (1974) The use of seed-banks for conservation of populations of species and ecotypes. *Biol. Conserv.* **6**, 15–19.